C000212921

SI

Wonderland

"How did you come here, to the land of shadows?"
HOMER The Odyssey, Book XI

"There live pallid Disease, dejected Age,
Fear, Hunger the bad counsellor, ugly Want,
Terrible spectres, Death and Decline."
VIRGIL The Aeneid, Book VI

Shadows in
Wonderland

a Hospital Odyssey

Colin Ludlow

Hammersmith Press
London, UK

First published in 2008 by Hammersmith Press Ltd,
496 Fulham Palace Road, London SW6 6JD, UK
www.hammersmithpress.co.uk
© Colin Ludlow 2008

Author's note
The central story in this book is my own but I have changed
the names of some individuals within it in order to protect
their identities. The Royal Free Hospital, London, UK is
described with the permission of the Royal Free Hampstead
NHS Trust after reading the manuscript.

British Library Cataloguing in Publication Data:
A CIP record of this book is available from the British
Library.

ISBN 978-1-905140-20-6

Designed by Amina Dudhia
Production by Helen Whitehorn, Pathmedia
Proof read by Brackley Proofreading Services
Typeset by Phoenix Photosetting, Chatham, Kent
Printed and bound by T J International Ltd of Padstow,
    Cornwall, UK
Cover image: Shadow of ladder on green grass by
    Charlie Fawell/Digital Vision/Getty Images

CONTENTS

ACKNOWLEDGEMENTS

Gillie Bolton may not have been the "only begetter" of this book, but it was she who prompted me to start writing about my hospital experiences, and her enthusiasm for what I produced that persuaded me to pursue the subject further. I owe her a huge debt of gratitude. I would also like to thank Polly McDonald, Paul Marcus, Howard Schuman, Stephen Wakelam, Jim Smith and Fiona Watt, whose encouragement and engagement with the ideas I was developing made me believe that they might interest a wider audience. Their comments on the manuscript were invaluable, as were those of Judith Murdoch, Nina Bawden, Richard Bull, Stephen Wyatt, Emma Oxley, Michael Moszynski, Sophie Balhetchet, Colin Luke, Antony Gormley and Nigel Ludlow.

Pam Solomon provided crucial help in moving the text towards publication. I am grateful to her and to Louisa Saunders at *The Independent*, which first published versions of two of the chapters. Georgina Bentliff at Hammersmith Press has been a most supportive and helpful publisher. My thanks are due to her as well.

I would also like to acknowledge the following copyright material that I have quoted in the book: *The Boys from the Blackstuff* by Alan Bleasdale, reproduced by permission of the author; *Waiting for Godot* by Samuel Beckett, published by Faber and Faber Ltd; *The Singing Detective* by Dennis Potter, published by Faber and Faber Ltd; *Saturday* by Ian McEwan, published by Jonathan Cape, reprinted by permission of The Random House Group; *Destiny* by Tim Parks, published by Vintage, reprinted by permission of the author (© Tim Parks 1999); *The Unbearable Lightness of Being* by Milan Kundera, published by Faber and Faber Ltd; *Blood and Guts* by Roy Porter, reproduced by permission of Penguin Books Ltd; *Cancer Ward* by Aleksandr Solzhenitsyn, published by The Bodley Head Ltd, reprinted by permission of The Random House Group Ltd; *Hippocratic Oaths* by Raymond Tallis, published by Atlantic Books; *The National Health* by Peter Nichols, published by Faber and Faber Ltd, reprinted by permission of the author; *The Magic Mountain* by Thomas Mann, published by Secker & Warburg, reprinted by permission of The Random House Group; *The Diving-Bell and the Butterfly* by Jean-Dominique Bauby, published by Fourth Estate, reprinted by permission of Harper Collins Publishers Ltd; *Snake Oil and Other Preoccupations* by John Diamond, published by Vintage, reprinted by permission of The Random House Group Ltd; *Illness as Metaphor* and *AIDS and Its Metaphors* by Susan Sontag, reproduced by permission of Penguin Books Ltd; *Non-Places: Introduction to an Anthropology of Supermodernity* by Marc Augé, published by Verso; *Howards End* by E M Forster reprinted by permission of the Society of Authors. Every effort has been made to trace the copyright holders. The publishers will be happy to correct any mistakes or omissions in future editions.

There is much in these pages that might be deemed critical of our hospital system, but I more than anyone am aware that I owe my life to the skill and care of the doctors and other staff at the Royal Free who looked after me. I wish to place on record the immense gratitude that I feel towards them.

Finally, I must express my heartfelt thanks to Anna, my wife, and our sons, Adam and Edmund, for their unfailing love and support. In many ways this is their story as much as my own, and if I have survived to tell it that is due to the light and inspiration they have always provided through the darkest of times. While I might rail against fate in many respects, I know that in having them as my closest family I have enjoyed unmatched and unchanging good fortune.

CHAPTER
1

THE GARDEN

"Methought I stood where trees of every clime,
Palm, myrtle, oak, and sycamore, and beech,
With plantain, and spice-blossoms, made a screen –
In neighbourhood of fountains, by the noise
Soft-showering in my ears, and, by the touch
Of scent, not far from roses."
JOHN KEATS The Fall of Hyperion. A Dream.

It is April, and suddenly spring has arrived. The winter was hard and protracted, with heavy snow in March, but now the sun is out, the temperature soaring, and the world is bursting with life.

Anna appears in my hospital room pushing a wheelchair. "I'm going to take you out," she announces, smiling. I look at her blankly. I have not set foot outside the building since being admitted in the bitter days of early January. This seems a rather rash idea.

"I thought we could go and sit in the hospital garden," she continues, undeterred by my lack of enthusiasm.

"All right," I eventually reply. I feel a little bewildered by this disruption to my customary routine, but lack the independence or strength to resist it.

Within a few minutes, a nurse has been summoned, my drips disconnected, and we are in the lift on our way downwards from my ninth-floor hideaway. Anna wheels me swiftly along the maze of corridors and out through the hospital entrance into the fresh air for the first time in more than three months. It hits me like a cool wave.

She pushes me across the front of the building, and then starts up the steep slip-road that leads to the car park and hospital garden. Here her pace soon slows due to the incline, and when we come to a speed bump in the roadway she stops entirely. Although my wasted body weighs no more than seven stones, she cannot gain sufficient momentum to push me and the rickety wheelchair over the hump. We are stuck.

Fortunately, a passing stranger comes to our aid. Having helped propel the chair over the stubborn mound that is blocking our progress, he then takes over completely and races on to the top of the slope. There he hands me back to Anna, and we turn to our left to enter the garden.

This is, in truth, a pretty modest affair. An oval of grass the size of a couple of cricket pitches or a championship golf green, with an asphalt path surrounding it and some flower beds outside this which contain shrubs and a few trees to shelter the whole space from the adjacent roads and buildings. There is a constant hum of traffic, and the air is thick with the city. But to me, this afternoon, it comes as a revelation.

The ripening spring grass seems unbelievably thick and green. The leaves on the trees and bushes are breaking forth in overwhelming and unparalleled abundance. All I can hear is the sound of the birds in full-throated chorus. The sun feels blissfully warm and soothing as it caresses my pale skin for the first time in months. I become intoxicated with the wonder of it all.

I shift from the wheelchair onto one of the garden benches donated "in loving memory" of some past patient, then sit in silence drinking in the impressions that are bombarding me. It may be due to my poor physical condition, but I find myself strangely breathless. All thoughts and fears ebb away as I surrender to the here and now, and experience the world as if for the first time. It is a marvellously healing sensation.

After 15 or 20 minutes, I begin to feel cold. Although the sun is hot, the earth and air are still cool from the winter. I am wearing only a fleece over my flimsy hospital smock and torn silk dressing gown, and my emaciated frame has no reserves of fat to keep it warm. "I think I'd better go back inside," I tell Anna reluctantly.

She pushes me back down the slope, and, with spirits sagging, I enter the cavernous building once more, bound for my eyrie up above. My journey through the hospital system, which originally started some two and a half years ago, is not over yet. I am still a long way from home.

CHAPTER
2

A BREAK WITH TRADITION

"These that have turned the world upside down are come hither"

The Acts of the Apostles, 17:6

During the First World War my grandfather served as an orderly in the Royal Army Medical Corps. He never talked in detail about his experiences, but he amused my brothers and me with the snippets of French he acquired at the time, which were trippingly delivered in a 'Cor-Blimey' London accent worthy of Eliza Doolittle (for, like her, he hailed from the streets of Lisson Grove). He also often mentioned travelling on a hospital train that ran back and forth between 'Ee-Taps' (Étaples) and Mar-Sails (Marseille).

However, he must have seen some pretty horrific things during his time in France for it left him with a lifelong fear of hospitals. His dying words to my mother, as he succumbed to a fatal heart attack some 60 years after the armistice, were "You won't let them take me away, will you Betty?" Happily, his final wish was granted. He died, relatively peacefully at home, before either doctor or ambulance arrived.

My mother inherited his deep-rooted suspicion of doctors and hospitals. These were places where "they" cut you up, a necessary evil but one to be avoided if at all possible. She had to spend a few days in Hammersmith Hospital when I was in my early teens having some troublesome varicose veins removed, but my brothers and I were not encouraged to visit. Otherwise, both she and my father enjoyed good health, and so I reached my mid-40s with only a minimal knowledge of hospitals.

I spent a few days in the old Charing Cross Hospital as a child having my adenoids removed, but apart from this my experience was limited to watching *Dr Kildare* and *Emergency Ward 10* on television, and to making mercifully rare visits to ailing friends or elderly neighbours. I did attend the births of both my sons in the Maternity Unit of University College Hospital, but these joyous events brought me no understanding of hospitals as institutions for treating the sick. Sadly, however, this situation was not to last.

■ ■ ■

It is Friday 10 November 2000 – a date to be engraved on my memory forever. Anna, my wife, has just returned from the Royal Free Hospital in Hampstead after a routine out-patient appointment for haemorrhoids, from which she has suffered since the birth of our second son some six years before. I am working at home that day (one of the joys of being freelance), and reading when she enters our study.

"Would you like to go out for lunch?" she enquires in a slightly cracked voice.

I look up in surprise.

"Only I've got a tumour in my bowel that's either cancerous or precancerous."

Her eyes fill with tears as I try to grasp what she is saying. Momentarily lost for words, I simply stand up and embrace her. I don't realize it at the time but I am about, in Susan Sontag's words, "to emigrate to the kingdom of the ill and live there".

Within days of learning that Anna's problem isn't haemorrhoids at all but something far more serious, I visit the hospital several times, accompanying her as she goes for various tests and then back to see the Consultant Surgeon for the results. He soberly tells us that the tumour *is* malignant, but that mercifully the cancer does not seem to have spread. We are unsure whether to feel relieved or appalled. However, I wake up the next morning with a feeling of profound sadness. I realize that innocence has been lost. Life will never be the same again.

Within three weeks I am visiting the hospital on a daily basis as Anna undergoes an operation to have the offending section of bowel removed. She looks dreadful in the aftermath of surgery and endures considerable pain, but recovers quickly and after 11 days is allowed home. I drive her back, crawling at a snail's pace over the speed bumps on the way, as each impact causes agony to the tender flesh around her wound. However, a week or so later we return to the hospital for a post-operative consultation, and the surgeon tells us that having examined the tumour they now consider chemotherapy is desirable as adjuvant therapy for her cancer. So two days after Christmas, our children are dispatched to play with friends for several hours while I escort Anna to the first of 24 weekly infusions of the toxic drug Fluorouracil.

After six months of these gruelling chemotherapy sessions, we hope that our crash course in hospitals might be coming to an end. But Anna's operation has involved the creation of an ileostomy to allow the bowel to heal, which now needs to be reversed if she is to regain the normal use of her body. Unfortunately, however, there is an anxiety that a "fistula" (an unfamiliar medical term for a channel or passage which will come to haunt me) has been created between her bowel and uterus. This means that re-connecting her bowel may result in highly unpleasant leakage between the two organs.

We consequently begin another round of hospital visits as the doctors attempt to establish the cause of the problem. This involves a gynaecological examination under general anaesthetic, highly specialized and unusual X-rays, a painful colonoscopy, and even a referral for a second opinion to the Hospital for Fistulas at Northwick Park in Harrow. (Neither us had ever heard of a fistula up to this point in our lives; now we discover there is actually a hospital specialising in their treatment.)

Even after all these investigations, however, the doctors are none the wiser. So in the absence of any conclusive evidence that a fistula *does* definitely exist, it is eventually decided to reverse the ileostomy and see what happens. Almost two years to the day after her original operation, Anna returns to the hospital for the necessary surgery. Happily, the reversal is successful and no unpleasant complications ensue.

There is no fistula.

But on the day after her operation I make my way from visiting Anna who is recuperating on the ninth floor of the building to an appointment of my own with her surgeon on the first. Mr Thomas is a huge black man with a rich deep voice – more like a booming operatic bass or some genial African chieftain than a conventional, clinically detached hospital consultant. He does a double-take when I enter the consulting room, and is clearly somewhat bemused to be dealing with me as a patient rather than as an accompanying relative. However, he listens attentively while I describe my symptoms, and then undertakes an examination. Once I have finished dressing, he tells me gravely, with no sign of his usual friendly smile: "You have a polyp in your bowel."

It is hard to know which of us is the more shocked. Lightning might not strike twice in the same place, but bowel cancer, it seems, is a different matter. I return to Anna in her bed up above and impart the grim news.

"He's not sure it's malignant," I say in an attempt to soften the blow.

Not surprisingly in her weakened state, she seems disinclined to take false comfort, but absorbs this latest disaster with weary resignation.

My own round of tests and investigations begins immediately as the hospital seeks to establish whether the growth is cancerous. A "flexible sigmoidoscopy" reveals that the tumour is one to two centimetres long, but the biopsies taken during the procedure prove less than conclusive. "Severe dysplasia" is the cryptic diagnosis Mr Thomas delivers when he telephones me with the results. I have already lived through Anna's cancer, however, and know what this means: dysplasia is the stage that cells go through before they become truly cancerous. A polyp showing mild dysplasia is one the doctors will continue to watch; one with moderate or severe dysplasia is one that ought to be removed.

So four weeks later I am admitted as an in-patient for an identical operation to the one that Anna had two years before. Having scarcely been discharged after the surgery to reverse her ileostomy, Anna now finds herself back at the hospital on a daily basis visiting me.

■ ■ ■

I awake from the anaesthetic following my operation and am convulsed by a fit of violent shivering. This is perhaps a portent of things to come. Although a bowel re-section constitutes major surgery, it is a common and routine procedure. The 11 days that Anna spent in hospital for her operation are pretty much par for the course. I am not so lucky. When my tumour is examined fully after being removed, it does prove to be malignant, but the cancer is less advanced than Anna's. Nevertheless, I will not finally crawl home until five months later. And I nearly don't make it at all.

In the days following my surgery, I have a series of unexpected complications and my temperature soars. Eventually, I am carted off to the hospital's Intensive Therapy Unit where I spend several days unconscious on a ventilator. I have a second operation to remove a further section of my bowel, and then suffer massive internal haemorrhaging. Over one tumultuous weekend, I am given 45 units of blood in transfusions. Eventually, the doctors decide to try a rare clotting agent in a desperate attempt to staunch my bleeding, and Anna is told that if this fails to work by the second dose then there is no further hope for me. My children respond to the warning of my imminent death with storm-hardened calm. They are used to grim news by now.

I subsequently have yet another operation, then contract pneumonia, and spend a total of six weeks in Intensive Care before being returned to a regular ward where I continue to be drip-fed for a further six weeks and remain for another three months until I am finally allowed home. As if to confirm my unsought status as a hospital veteran, in the course of all this I even manage to catch the hospital "superbug", MRSA.

Sadly, but all too predictably, being discharged does not mark the end of my immersion in the murky depths of the hospital world either. During the course of my five month internship, I discover that I have developed a fistula (a real one this time, not merely symptoms that suggest one) between my small bowel and the surface of my abdomen. This means that I am, in effect, leaking excrement through a small tear in my stomach wall near where my navel once was, and when I leave hospital there is natural concern – not least my own – about how I will cope with this at home. I manage to do so for some time, but the problem gradually grows worse, and eventually requires surgery to repair it. Fifteen months after my escape from their suffocating embrace, I am forced to brave the hospital corridors once again as I undergo my fourth major operation.

In the meantime, my illness has also caused a further complication – a benign stricture in my oesophagus. This makes swallowing difficult. I am therefore forced to return to the hospital for treatment to deal with that as well, and I continue to have to do so on a regular basis.

■ ■ ■

This ongoing treatment has taken me to a series of exotic and unexpected locations. I have had short stays on wards with spare beds that actually specialize in ophthalmology, genito-urinary problems and ear, nose and throat surgery, as well as in the Day Surgery Unit. I have even spent two nights, courtesy of the NHS, in the hospital's private wing when that was the only place a bed was available. For other reasons I have been through the oncology, rheumatology, gasteroenterology, casualty and even gynaecology departments. I have had endoscopies, colonoscopies, fistulagrams, barium swallows, electro-cardiograms, CT scans, and blood tests for everything from AIDS to vasculitis; and, apart from doctors and nurses, I have been attended by dieticians, counsellors, physiotherapists, chaplains, even masseurs, reflexologists and a hypnotherapist.

In short I have had an unplanned but bizarrely wide-ranging exposure to the myriad facets of the modern hospital. This book is an account of that experience. As well as describing what happened physically – the medical trials and tribulations that Anna and I endured – it also traces the mental journey that I went on, to a host of distant places, as a result of my illness. For one of the curious things about infirmity is that when your body is rendered immobile, your mind still roams free, and you find you have an awful lot of time for thinking. By recording the scattered thoughts, memories, dreams and ideas that five years of voyaging through the medical system have provoked, this book seeks to convey what it means to be ill, what it means to live in the kingdom of the sick as a long-term hospital patient.

As a society we spend a great deal of money on healthcare, yet there seems to be desperately little imaginative understanding of the experience of illness in the way that our institutions are organized. The struggle against ill health is one that we all face at some point in our lives; but, sadly, that struggle is often made more desperate and difficult than it needs to be. Dealing with them from the inside, it is easy for those who work in hospitals to lose sight of just how strange and daunting they can seem to those who go there seeking treatment. But, perhaps for obvious reasons, the patients' voices that are generally heard on the subject, and on other healthcare issues, are not those of the chronically sick. Rather, they are those of journalists for whom illness is a temporary inconvenience, an annoying interruption of a busy schedule, not an ongoing burden that utterly transforms their lives. The experience of sustained ill health is a different one that raises fundamental, but strangely neglected, questions about the role and purpose of hospitals in our present-day world: what they actually are, and what they could or should be.

In the course of my prolonged exposure to the madness and magnificence of the NHS, I have been forced to confront these, and in chronicling that history I have consequently found myself drawing a portrait of a hospital – a highly coloured, partial and subjective portrait I have no doubt, but one that may at least capture something of the baffling, surreal and even occasionally comic nature of hospital life. I have written about what I know, where most of my experience was gained. But the more I hear of other people's experiences, the more I read about other institutions elsewhere, the more I realize that it could be almost any large, modern hospital that I am describing. The Royal Free, as it features in this book, is simply a paradigm, or emblem, for a pattern of healthcare that is to be found, not only in Britain, but around the entire globe. The details may vary, but the problems, as well the virtues, are – to use a medical term – systemic.

Hospitals distort time. As Thomas Mann vividly explores in his novel *The Magic Mountain*, the routines of treating illness both stretch and compress time to create a kind of "eternal present" in which normal chronology is lost. Add to this the fact that as a hospital patient you spend much of your time in a drug-fuelled haze, haphazardly negotiating a labyrinthine Wonderland where the extraordinary is routinely treated as commonplace, and it should come as no surprise to find that this narrative is fragmentary, disordered, even dream-like at times, ranging freely across the temporal sequence of events as it follows my internal wanderings. Even now I have no clear recollection of the exact order in which many of the events in these pages occurred. In many ways, these reflections are like so many shards of a shattered mirror that was once my life. In gathering them up and piecing them together, I have been forced to search for a different order to make sense of what remains than the purely external shape that time alone provides. These pages are the record of a quest – which no one can avoid entirely – of trying to achieve wholeness (a biblical synonym for health) in a fractured, disjointed world.

CHAPTER
3

PARKING

"DOCTOR: Ah, yes. The conspiracy theory. The whole world is against you.
YOSSER: That's not true. But you don't like me, do you?
DOCTOR: That's neither here nor there, Mr Hughes.
YOSSER: Nobody likes me."

ALAN BLEASDALE Boys from the Blackstuff

It is ten days or so since her tumour was diagnosed, and Anna is returning to hospital for an MRI scan. Her surgeon, Mr Thomas, wants as complete a picture as possible of what he is dealing with prior to operating, and fortunately the hospital is one of comparatively few in the country to be equipped with this extremely expensive facility. People come from far and wide and can often wait months to use it.

We agree that Anna will walk up to the hospital for the appointment, and that I will collect her afterwards by car in case the procedure leaves her feeling weak or tired. (The anxiety of being told she has cancer, never mind the physical effects of the illness, have already taken their toll and left her significantly depleted.)

At this time I fail to realize that the riot of double and triple-parked cars in front of the hospital's main entrance is the result of people in fact being allowed to leave their vehicles there for up to 20 minutes at a time while collecting or dropping off patients. So on arrival I go to look for a space in the hospital car park.

This is a small, two-storey block wedged into the hill on the side of the main building and topped out with the hospital garden on the roof. Given the explosion of car-use since the Royal Free was built and the price of real-estate in Hampstead, it is, unsurprisingly, woefully under-sized for the scale of the institution. The John Radcliffe Hospital on the outskirts of Oxford, a comparably vast edifice, boasts acres of parking space that is always awash with cars and gives the building the appearance of some immense craggy rock jutting out from a swirling ocean of vehicles. A similar car park in Hampstead would probably stretch over most of the Heath.

Taking cynical advantage of the disparity between supply and demand, the Royal Free actually charges more for its parking spaces than the very few meters available on the streets around the hospital. Nevertheless, the car park is invariably full, and this particular morning is no exception. I drive round a couple of times, desperately hunting for a space and growing increasingly anxious that it is already past the time when I have said I will collect Anna. Eventually, I notice that there are a few parking spaces on the access road at the back of the hospital. These are full too, but there is one small gap – just big enough for my car – in front of a tree. For some mysterious reason, though, this has criss-cross yellow lines hatched over it.

Aware that this probably means I shouldn't park there, but with seemingly no alternative, I slide my Golf into the gap, leap out, race across the hospital garden, career down the steps alongside the car park and crash through the entrance to the MRI suite which nestles below – only to discover Anna still sitting in the reception area waiting for her scan. They are running seriously late. I am still sufficiently inexperienced in the ways of hospitals to be slightly thrown by this, but quickly explain that I can't leave the car where it is and shall return shortly. I then run back full tilt to where it is parked.

I have been gone for at the most three minutes, but in that time, with an alacrity that would be welcome in the X-ray department, a burly member of the hospital's uniformed security staff together with two silent assistants has managed to appear from nowhere and place a parking clamp on one of the front wheels of my car. They are now busily tightening the screws. I pull up short in disbelief.

"Look, hang on a moment," I say. "I've only been gone a couple of minutes."

"You shouldn't be parked here," the uniformed guard replies.

"But why not?" I ask. "The car's not in anyone's way."

"It's needed for access," is the curt response. As the only access through the hatched space is into a tree, I find this a pretty unconvincing explanation. However, I don't think it will help matters to say so and opt instead to pursue the Guard's logic.

"Well, OK. If you let me go you'll be able to get access straightaway. If you clamp me it'll cause an obstruction for hours."

"It's too late now," the Guard snarls back, avoiding my eyes and clearly determined not to yield to any form of reasoning. "You'll have to pay the fine to get it removed," and he points to the £50 penalty notice on my windscreen.

During the past two weeks I have been unexpectedly told that my wife has serious bowel cancer. I have grappled with the possibility of life without her and endured the ordeal of telling our two children about her illness. Although only ten and six, their school-caretaker's son died of the same cancer a year ago and they are only too aware of its implications. I have also had to impart the grim news about her condition repeatedly to shocked family and friends. I have got through this with teeth-gritted determination – the dogged refusal to be overwhelmed by circumstances that comes from feeling you have no alternative. At no point have I cried or given way to self-pity.

Now, however, confronted by a clamp on my car, a fine I can ill afford to pay and an aggressively unpleasant security guard, I am suddenly struck by the feeling that life really is unfair and that the whole world is against me. As I fight back the tears, I find myself starting to rage against the universe like Yosser Hughes in the unforgettable 1980s' television drama *Boys from the Blackstuff*. I stridently inform the Guard that my wife has cancer and that she is down in X-ray now, waiting for me to collect her. I only left the car here for a couple of minutes because there was nowhere else to park. Doesn't he have any human feeling?

My howling and pleading are to no avail.

"You've made a mistake but you just won't admit to it," he

sanctimoniously informs me, determined not to concede the moral high ground. I know I am fighting a losing battle, but can no longer restrain myself. I demand to know his name and say I'm going to write to complain about his behaviour. He looks momentarily discomforted, but is not going to back off now and defiantly spits out his surname. Finally, possessed by a kind of hysterical energy, I storm off to find the hospital cashiers and pay my fine, complaining bitterly to anyone who will listen as I go.

Of course I don't have a cheque book with me or £50 in my wallet, so after discovering that they do not accept credit cards I am forced to go in search of a cash machine. Then I retrace my steps to the cashiers, queue again to make the payment, take the receipt to the security guards' office in the basement, and wait once more while they find someone to release the clamp.

It is some time before I find my way back to the X-ray department. There I discover Anna waiting patiently in the MRI reception, scan completed and with the radiographer sitting alongside her. I apologize for the delay and miserably recount my tale of woe. The radiographer is hugely embarrassed.

"If you write and explain what happened, I'm sure they'll refund your money," she says, clearly feeling guilty about the failure to deal with Anna at the appointed time and believing this to be the cause of the problem. "I'll confirm what you're saying if they want to ask me," she adds kindly.

I never do write to complain or ask for my money back. I have been trying to set up a long-term project at work for the past nine months and earnt nothing during that time. With Anna now about to stop work for an indefinite period, the cash is far from irrelevant. But with a sick wife about to go into hospital for a serious operation, two small children whose lives I am trying to hold together and my own work to keep going as best I can, there always seem to be more pressing things to do than pen angry letters to vent my sense of grievance.

CHAPTER
4

WONDERLAND

"It was neither an old stronghold nor a new mansion, but a rambling pile…if K. had not known that it was a castle he might have taken it for a little town."

FRANZ KAFKA The Castle

If you go to Berlin and make your way to the roof of the Reichstag building which is now topped by Norman Foster's magnificent glass dome, you are able to enjoy spectacular views across the city in all directions. Immediately to the south nestles the Brandenburg Gate; out to the west stretch the extensive greenery and war memorials of the Tiergarten; in the east the giant television tower that was erected as an assertion of Communist dynamism soars into the air; while the skyline to the north is dominated by the massive orange and grey bulk of a huge "office" block with a sign on the roof that spells out the word "Charité" in vivid red letters. But this building is not the headquarters of some giant, multi-national corporation flourishing its logo at the world; nor is it a legacy Soviet imperialism and power. It is the current home of Berlin's most celebrated hospital.

Perched halfway up Hampstead hill, fifteen storeys high and with no other high-rise buildings around it, the Royal Free Hospital dominates the north London skyline in much the same way. Look up the railway line from Camden Town, take a view north from the top of Primrose Hill, west from Dartmouth Park or south from Hampstead Heath, and there it is – a monolithic reminder of 1960s' brutalism. In the locality, it is sometimes sardonically referred to as the "Hampstead Hilton". The hotel analogy is an obvious one, but seems inspired more by its height and ugliness than anything else. Interestingly, the BBC's old rehearsal room building in West London, an equally unattractive edifice that once dwarfed the surrounding landscape, provoked the same response and used to be known as the "Acton Hilton".

Peter Baker, my local vicar who spends a lot of time at the Royal Free visiting ailing parishioners, likens it to an airport. This is chiefly on account of its international quality, for the building teems with patients, visitors and staff from all over the world. The situation has changed slightly since smoking was banned anywhere on the hospital site, but as you approach the entrance it seems to disgorge a chaotic mass of humanity, many in pyjamas or hospital gowns, all seeking to steal a quick cigarette or grab a breath of fresh air uncontaminated by the building's superannuated air-conditioning system. Pass through the milling crowd of different nationalities that clogs the doors and enter the reception area with its waiting taxi-drivers on your way to the ground-floor cafeteria – which is all formica-covered tables and coloured cardboard cups filled with half-drunk cappuccinos – and you could easily be at Heathrow or almost any other airport in the world.

My own imagination is more baroque, however. The huge building, permanently under construction from great concrete slabs and with its mass of polyglot inhabitants, reminds me of Pieter Brueghel's famous painting of *The Tower of Babel*; while the cash-machines and car-parks, the tea-bars and uniformed security staff recall to my mind another self-contained Wonderland – namely, the curious world of BBC Television Centre, where I worked in the Drama Department as a script editor and subsequently producer during the late 1980s and early 1990s. This is also a maze-like institutional building, dating from the 1960s, that seems both familiar and yet unreal and forbidding at the same time.

However, these comparisons – which might be made with almost any modern hospital – are based largely on externals. After spending much time there, and for reasons I shall explain in due course, the Royal Free now seems to me more like Prague (that is to say Kafka's) Castle. By extension, in my own head it also resembles a prison.

Like the Charité in Berlin, where Rudolph Virchow conducted his ground-breaking work on cellular pathology that provides the basis of our modern understanding of cancer during the 1840s and 1850s, the Royal Free boasts a long and distinguished history. The hospital was founded in 1828 by William Marsden, a young surgeon who later also founded the celebrated cancer hospital that still bears his name. The Royal Free thus celebrated its 175th anniversary at Easter 2003, and all the in-patients at the time – of whom I was one – were given a com-memorative egg-cup, rather bizarrely and inadequately filled with a Cadbury's Crème Egg, to mark the event.

The hospital's name reflects its original mission to provide free care to those who could not afford treatment, and for a long time it was the only hospital in Britain to do so. Its declared policy was that "disease and poverty shall alone be the passports to relief", and although it should be remembered in the early 19th century the rich kept well away from hospitals, it proved extremely popular with those who were impoverished and acutely ill. Within a decade of opening its doors, the hospital was treating some 14,000 patients a year. By admitting the types of patient that other institutions preferred to turn away – includ-ing those suffering from venereal disease – Marsden incurred consid-erable hostility from the medical establishment and the governors of other hospitals, but he pressed on undeterred. After distinguishing itself by being the only hospital in the capital to remain open and treat the victims during the cholera epidemic that hit London in 1832, it was granted a royal charter five years later, and the "Free Hospital" acquired the "Royal" moniker without which no self-respecting British institution seems to regard itself as complete.

The hospital continued its relentless growth throughout the 19th and into the 20th century. The present building, which opened to patients in 1974 and boasts a floor area three times that of Norman Foster's towering "Gherkin" skyscraper in the City of London, is the result of the old Royal Free Hospital in Gray's Inn Road "merging" – like some voracious corporate raider – with the New End, North-Western Fever and Hampstead General hospitals. Some of the title and foundation stones of these earlier incarnations now adorn the hospital garden, mossily peeking out of the surrounding grass like abandoned and misshapen gravestones. And a semi-circular cast-iron grille that once filled the entrance arch in Gray's Inn Road and reads "Royal Free Hospital 1894" hangs from the front wall of the current building, greeting cars at the head of the access road as they turn forlornly to left and right in vain pursuit of a parking space. Nothing remains, however, of the Elizabeth Garrett Anderson Hospital, which once numbered among its subsidiaries. That was "traded on" in 1974 and now forms part of neighbouring University College Hospital.

Like other major hospitals, the Royal Free is not just an institution for treating the sick formed by consolidating several smaller establishments. It also comprises a medical school and extensive research facilities. It is a vast, high-profile enterprise with over 1,000 beds and an annual budget of £350 million. (To put this in some sort of perspective, that is roughly three and half times what the local borough of Camden spends on all its schools in the course of a year, or what it costs the BBC to fund its entire News output from around the world over a 12-month period.) The hospital treats more than half a million patients each year, or roughly 10,000 each week. Of these some 120,000 are day or in-patients, 340,000 are out-patients and 76,000 are Accident and Emergency cases (although having been all three myself in the course of one recent 12-month period I suspect these figures may include a little double counting).

It possesses an award-winning Stroke Unit, state of the art kidney facilities, and has developed ground-breaking treatments in a number of different fields. As an "acute trust", it offers top-level care for a large number of specialisms to patients from all over the country. I possibly owe my life to the hospital's expertise in dealing with haemophilia, and its consequently bountiful supplies of blood and sophisticated blood products. It also has "frontline" status, and a number of the victims of the July 7 bombings in 2005 were consequently taken there for treatment.

On the educational side, it was for many years the only hospital in England prepared to offer clinical facilities for training women doctors. This pioneering commitment began in 1877 when, despite opposition from the medical profession, the public and even Queen Victoria herself, the hospital board agreed to open its wards to students from the London School of Medicine for Women. The school was subsequently absorbed into the hospital, and Elizabeth Garrett Anderson – the only female member of the British Medical Association from 1874 until 1893 – was subsequently appointed as the first in a succession of seven women deans.

Throughout its history, the hospital has been no stranger to controversy, and that tradition continues to the present day. Among its many research staff past and present working on a huge variety of subjects, it numbered Dr Andrew Wakefield, who created a furore when he published a paper in *The Lancet* in 1998 suggesting links between the MMR vaccine, bowel disorders and autism, and followed this up in a press conference at the hospital at which he called for the combined measles, mumps and rubella vaccine to be split into three separate ones. More recently it hit the headlines when it was one of the first hospitals to announce bed closures and staff cuts in order to cope with the financial crisis that engulfed many health service trusts in 2006. A year later, it was celebrated by the government for turning a £30 million deficit into a £15 million surplus, thus helping eliminate the NHS overspend.

The Royal Free is constantly in the public eye, and as the largest single-site teaching hospital in London, it represents the very embodiment of the modern "superhospital". It is a vast, expensive flagship of medicine at its most advanced; a teeming, zealously watched shrine for all that contemporary healthcare has to offer; an ever-expanding Wonderland with its own inexorable logic and resource-devouring momentum. Unfortunately for the patient, however, big is not always beautiful, and teeming shrines may not make the most comfortable of dwellings.

CHAPTER
5

WAITING

"They also serve who only stand and wait."
JOHN MILTON Sonnet XIX: On his blindness

I sometimes think the bulk of my life has been spent waiting.

███

Of course there is a view of human existence that sees life as simply "Death's waiting room". Our lives are passed in a kind of Beckettian paralysis that renders us passive and trapped, unable to act or progress, desperately hoping for some external intervention that will give them shape or meaning.

███

But the waiting I am talking about is far more literal than that. I suppose it began as a student, waiting for exam results that would determine the next phase of my life. Waiting to see which university might accept me turned into waiting to land a job that would offer some sort of satisfaction or fulfilment. Meanwhile I was waiting to find a girlfriend, waiting to see whether this relationship might have a long-term future or even be the basis for marriage.

When I became a drama producer this kind of waiting stepped up a gear and seemed to become daily and routine. Waiting for writers to deliver their scripts; waiting for executives to read those scripts and give my projects the go-ahead; waiting for directors, designers or cameramen to say they would like to work on my productions; waiting for actors to accept the parts they had been offered or agree their fees; waiting for filming to start, waiting for filming to finish; waiting to view the first cut; waiting for executive approval of the finished programme; waiting for transmission; waiting for the reactions of press, peers and public.

■ ■ ■

All of which ought to have prepared me for my exposure to hospitals and life among the long-term sick. For to be a hospital patient – as the very word itself suggests – means to wait. Wait for an appointment to see a consultant; wait for X-rays or tests; wait for results; wait for your operation; wait to see if it has been successful; wait to get better. But there is one crucial distinction between this kind of waiting and the waiting I had experienced in the earlier part of my life. Whereas any phase of that would eventually be followed by – or indeed precipitate – a new period of activity (frequently of great intensity which made the delay in commencing it all the more frustrating), the end of each wait in a hospital context seems only to be followed by more waiting.

■ ■ ■

The nature of illness is such that the vexations of waiting in most other contexts seem pretty trivial by comparison. It is Sunday, two days after Anna has been told that she has a tumour in her bowel that may be malignant. We are awaiting the results of the biopsy that will determine this. Meanwhile her family gathers for the christening of our nephew. Rightly or wrongly, we elect not to spoil the party by announcing the news which so shocked us only two days before – particularly since we are as yet uncertain exactly what that news is. A benign tumour is one thing; cancer something else. However, photographs of the event will later reveal quite clearly the strain that we are under. My face is taut with anxiety; Anna's half-hearted smiles have a melancholy wistfulness that suggests an underlying dread that these may be among the last pictures that will ever be taken of her.

The next day, she receives a phone call from the hospital's X-ray department asking her to go in for an urgent CT scan. Although the caller says no more than this, Anna and I both know then that she has cancer. On the Tuesday I take her to the hospital, and while she is waiting for the scan we catch sight of Mr Thomas, the surgeon who examined her a few days before. Taking pity on our evident concern and distress, he tells us where we can find him after Anna has had her X-ray, and later he reveals that, yes, her tumour is malignant. The CT scan is to see how far the cancer has spread and whether it is operable.

"You mean it might already be terminal?" Anna exclaims, horrified.

"Look, let's be positive," Mr Thomas replies, trying to reassure us. "You don't look like someone with advanced cancer." This seems less than wholly convincing, but he can offer little further comfort other than to tell us to come and see him in his clinic on the following Friday when he will know the results of the scan. We both spend the next three days feeling that Anna is like a convicted criminal awaiting sentence: is it to be the death penalty or will there be some form of reprieve? Inevitably, we fear the worst.

On the Friday we arrive at the hospital at the appointed time, only to be greeted by a handwritten notice on the whiteboard above the clinic receptionist's head which reads: "Mr Thomas – clinic running 60-90 minutes late." Having already spent a week in turmoil, this further extension of our wait seems particularly cruel. Unable to bear the dreadful passivity of sitting patiently in the hospital for the next hour and a half, we elect to fill the time in a café across the road. God knows what we drink or find to talk about, but eventually we return to the hospital and are ushered into a small treatment room where I sit with my fingers pathetically crossed in my pocket as we wait to hear the news from Mr Thomas. In the context it is "good". "There are no metastases," is the way he puts it. The tumour is about three centimetres long, but no secondary growths are apparent. "All" that Anna faces is a major operation to remove the tumour in less than a fortnight's time.

But of course, as anyone who has lived with cancer will know, the agony of waiting does not end there. After the operation and being discharged, Anna returns to the same clinic for the results of the histology on the tumour that has been removed. This time the news is less encouraging: although all visible signs of cancer have now been cut out, the growth has affected several lymph nodes and the oncologist therefore proposes six months of chemotherapy to help prevent any malignancy recurring.

And so we embark on a further routine of waiting. Each week before her treatment and at quarterly intervals once the course has been completed, Anna has a blood test to check for any signs of the cancer renewing itself. The oncology doctors are well trained to give the results of the tests at the start of their consultations, but each visit carries with it the anxiety that this time you won't hear the reassuring words, "Your bloods are fine."

This is particularly true if there have been any other causes for concern since the last appointment. Some four years after completing her chemotherapy, Anna develops a worrying combination of repeated bouts of tiredness with a blood test that suggests her white cell count is abnormally low. Then a tiny polyp is found in her bowel during a routine colonoscopy. As we sit in the oncology clinic waiting for the results of the biopsy, I am uncomfortably thrown back to my imagined feelings of the prisoner at his trial – but this time awaiting the jury's verdict rather than the judge's sentence. My fingers are once again firmly crossed in my pocket as the doctor tells Anna that the cancer markers in her blood are fine.

"But what about the biopsy?" she enquires anxiously. "They found a cyst during my colonoscopy." The doctor looks slightly bemused and thumbs through Anna's notes. "The results aren't here," she tells us. "Hold on. I'll go and check on the computer." She leaves the room for what seems like an age. We sit in tense silence. Our minds are focused on just one thing, incapable of distraction. Eventually the doctor returns.

"Sorry about that," she says calmly, apparently unmindful of our tension.

"The biopsy's clear. There are no cell abnormalities."

I smile politely, but really want to hug both the doctor and Anna to express my relief.

In the early 1980s I worked at Riverside Studios, the arts centre in West London. During my time there, Samuel Beckett came to the Studios from Paris to rehearse the San Quentin Drama Workshop in a production of *Waiting for Godot*. This extraordinary theatre company was formed in 1957 by Rick Cluchey, a convict who was then serving a life sentence in San Quentin Prison (California's state penitentiary). He was inspired to do so after he had seen a performance of Beckett's celebrated play given to the prison inmates by a group of professional actors from San Francisco. At that time, although the play had enjoyed both critical and commercial success, it was viewed by audiences on both sides of the Atlantic with a certain degree of bafflement. But the prisoners – who obviously knew a thing or two about waiting – had no such problem and responded to the drama with intuitive understanding. In Cluchey's words: "the place exploded with laughter. There was an immediate connection!"

So great was the impact that Cluchey promptly asked the authorities for permission to start a prison theatre company. This was granted, though with the proviso that performances did not involve any female impersonations (evidently viewed as dangerous provocation). *Godot*, with its all-male cast, thus became an obvious text for the company to work on, and the prisoners' production of the play – informed by their natural empathy with the material – went on to achieve widespread acclaim. It soon came to the attention of Beckett himself, and over the years that followed he worked with the San Quentin Drama Workshop on several different productions of his plays, one of which was the staging rehearsed at Riverside.

The Royal Free Hospital has its own Music Society that regularly gives public performances, but not, to my knowledge, a Drama Workshop. Were it to do so, however, I suspect that a production of *Waiting for Godot* by the patients might prove equally riveting. The play no longer mystifies its audiences, but those who have been exposed for any length of time to the hospital system are likely to appreciate its meaning with a very particular intensity, and perform it with an instinctive depth of understanding comparable to the San Quentin prisoners.

Learning to wait is a crucial part of being ill, but it is possible to wait *too* patiently.

It is summer 2000. Anna is beginning to be troubled with recurrent symptoms of haemorrhoids and goes to see our GP. He says he will refer her to a specialist at the Royal Free. Weeks go by without her hearing anything further. At the same time we are bombarded by constant articles in the press about National Health Service waiting lists. We simply put the delay down to routine problems and inefficiency. Eventually, after more than three months with no word from the hospital, Anna decides to chase the matter up again with the GP. Investigations are made at the surgery. These reveal that owing to an administrative oversight the GP's letter of referral has never been sent. It is now, and an appointment comes through quite quickly. But when Anna attends this and is told that her problem is not swollen haemorrhoids but a bowel tumour, we are left wondering how much further the cancer may have spread during those wasted months. We bitterly regret paying too much attention to the negative publicity of the media, as a result of which we have not bothered to follow up the matter sooner.

Interestingly, when I go to the GP's surgery two years later with similar symptoms, the doctor informs me that a government guideline has recently been introduced that now makes it obligatory for me to be seen at the hospital within two weeks. To my relief I am. And I firmly believe that the innovation of setting a time limit is a good one, even though it may not be to everyone's benefit. For, as a result of my late addition to his list, on this particular Friday Mr Thomas's clinic is overbooked, and some other poor soul has perhaps to endure a further 90 minutes of agony waiting for the results of his or her CT scan.

■ ■ ■

I am sitting on a plastic chair in an airless room lit by tubes of perspex-covered neon. Anna sits alongside me. We are waiting – and have been for well over an hour. I have long since exhausted my interest in the three-year-old copy of *Good Housekeeping* that I found on the seat next to mine. I look up wearily to see a man with a briefcase pass into the reception area.

"That's Mr Kasionis," murmurs Anna. He exchanges a few words with the clinic clerk, then swiftly vanishes through the Exit doors and down the stairs. "I guess I won't be seeing *him* today," Anna adds with a clear note of frustration in her voice. Other people who arrived later than we did have been called in ahead of us, but we were consoling ourselves with the hope that they were seeing members of the consultant's team rather than the man himself.

Anna glances at her watch.

"I should have been seen two hours ago," says the young woman next to her, reading her thoughts. Anna is wondering whether to ring her colleagues at work and warn them that she will probably be late for their meeting.

"I'd better ask what's going on," she says, and makes her way to the reception desk. Our younger son will soon be back from school. I am thinking that I ought to call and let him know why no one is at home, but a sign on the wall forbids me to use my mobile phone as it interferes with the hospital equipment, and I am reluctant to step outside and risk missing our turn.

"She thinks it'll be another three quarters of an hour," Anna returns to inform me. "Apparently the first appointment took half an hour longer than expected." I wonder how this explains a two-hour delay, but say nothing. This is not a rational universe. It defies our attempts to make sense of it. So I just take a deep breath and try not to give way to my mounting sense of annoyance and anxiety.

The world of the sick moves painfully slowly, and the cumbersome machinery of its institutions grinding on their way is painfully at odds with the urgency felt by those requiring their assistance. As a patient, you spend far more time waiting than actually using the Health Service's facilities and resources. All the more important then that those running hospitals pay as much attention to what happens *before* you see the doctor, radiographer or phlebotomist as when you do. As Beckett's tramps, Vladimir and Estragon, so poignantly reveal in *Waiting for Godot,* it is hard to wait with dignity and equanimity. To do that you need to be kept informed: to know who you are waiting for and why; to know how long that wait will be and the reason for any delays; to understand why others are apparently being seen "out of turn", and to be convinced that the waiting system is fair. You also need a comfortable and proper place in which to wait, not be perched in a corridor or find yourself obstructing a doorway. As a sick person, you do not want to waste your limited energy standing because there are insufficient seats. People have feelings that inevitably run high when they fear their lives are under threat. Their fragile health and sense of well-being will inevitably be undermined if their waiting is indefinitely protracted by repeatedly cancelled operations, contemptuously missed appointment times, thoughtlessly ill-managed priorities, or any other form of neglect.

And the sad fact is that all too often, in hospitals as in so many spheres of life, selfishness and bad behaviour find themselves rewarded. It is the difficult patient who makes a fuss that is seen more quickly – or at least keeps his place in the queue and is not forgotten or overlooked – not the docile, accepting one who declines to question the inscrutable reasons for delay.

■ ■ ■

"ESTRAGON: So long as one knows.
VLADIMIR: One can bide one's time.
ESTRAGON: One knows what to expect.
VLADIMIR: No further need to worry.
ESTRAGON: Simply wait.
VLADIMIR: We're used to it."

CHAPTER
6

BUILDINGS

"[The annexe] faces the hospital, and its back looks into a field
from which it is separated only by the grey hospital fence
studded with nails. The nails, their sharp points sticking
upwards, the fence and the annexe itself have that special kind
of depressing, baneful air which is so characteristic of our
hospitals and prison buildings."

ANTON CHEKHOV Ward 6

Architecturally the Royal Free Hospital belongs not in Hampstead with
its elegant 18th century cottages and villas, but amid the soaring, concrete monstrosities of East Croydon. It is an ugly, box-like building,
exemplifying 1960s' design and materials at their most depressing,
unredeemed even by a purposeful sense of efficient functionality.

Despite being composed on a modernist grid made up of straight
lines and right angles, the building is a maze-like structure which is
confusingly laid out and hard to find one's way around. Perhaps significantly, the main entrance leads into the hospital sideways. Confronted
by the plants and brightly-coloured helium balloons on sale in the shop
opposite as you make your way through the front doors, you are forced

to make a 90-degree turn into the reception area, which simply brings you face to face with a bewildering array of signs and lines on the floor intended to assist your onward progress through the building. To reach the main lifts requires a complicated zig-zag through a set of swing doors, past the toilets and down a long gallery hung with rather garish paintings for sale by local amateur artists. There is another group of lifts through a different set of swing doors that lie directly ahead of you in the entrance hall, but these only go as far as the second floor or down to the Accident and Emergency Department in the basement.

The building has been designed without proper or sufficient waiting areas. The result is that many of its narrow corridors are clogged with crowds of patients waiting for their appointments. They spill out messily from tiny groups of seats while queuing to have their blood or X-rays taken like the clamouring supplicants in some scene from a Kafka novel. In his 1985 television film *The Insurance Man,* Alan Bennett (a local resident) memorably depicted the Workers Accident Insurance Institute in Prague where the great Czech novelist worked. The mysterious and confusing building, crammed with sick and disabled people all fighting desperately for the attention of the staff, might have been inspired by the Royal Free. Equally, Bennett might have been describing one of the hospital's patients when he wrote of the film's hero: "His quest [to find the kindly Dr Kafka] gets him lost in the huge building where his adventures take on the overtones of K's experiences in *The Trial* and also of Alice in *Through the Looking Glass.*"

The surreal, dream-like quality of the hospital building is compounded by the fact that many of its staff seem to work in cupboards. Keith, the exotically-titled "Complementary Therapies Co-ordinator", gives calming massages in a tiny, windowless closet on the eighth floor, the doors of which appear designed for a store room rather one intended for human occupation. Similarly, Gabriella, the colorectal nurse housed on the floor above, receives patients and goes about her business in a small, softly-lit box lined with a cornucopia of stoma bags, water-resistant creams and soothing powders. Both emerge, mole-like, from their cupboards, blinking furiously, but not into daylight – merely into the more brightly illuminated enclosure of the main hospital corridors.

For one of the other defining features of the Royal Free building is its pervasive and depressing absence of natural light. The ground and lower-ground floors are entirely window-free zones, with the result that the Casualty Department seems like a badly-lit stage set, while the main lobby through which you enter the building immediately transports the incoming patient or visitor into an atmosphere of Stygian gloom. There have been attempts recently to improve the lighting, and the corridors throughout the ground floor are decorated with murals, paintings and contemporary prints. But in the face of low ceilings and drab walls, and without the assistance of anything natural such as plants, sunlight or fresh air, they struggle vainly to lift the mood of oppressive grimness. A walk, or worse still a wheelchair ride, to the X-ray Department is a singularly dispiriting experience.

Even the upper storeys share the same problem. Although the rooms on the outside of the building enjoy wonderful views, such is the bulk of the edifice that the wards and corridors at its centre are shut off from daylight and similarly project a mood of dim, artificially-lit bleakness.

Because of its size and verticality, the hub of the building is its battery of passenger lifts. These six elevators, housed in a lift-well that is curiously off-centre and inaccessible, are the arteries that keep the building alive and functioning. Crowded, enclosed, showing signs of wear and tear, and often not all working, they are perhaps a microcosm of the hospital as a whole. But whatever their shortcomings, these public lifts with their engraved, if out-of-date, floor guides are positively handsome and state-of-the-art compared with the hospital's bed-lifts for patients which resemble the creaking backstage goods' lifts of some faded department store. Although there are several of these, no more than a couple ever seem to be in use. However, given their battered, lurching interiors, floor buttons that seem to hang off the matt metal walls, and blue-painted doors which judder open and closed, it is perhaps a miracle that any of them work at all. As it is, they each require a dedicated lift operator to coax them into life.

While lying in my bed on the ninth floor, I often wonder what would happen in the event of a serious fire. It would take hours to evacuate the hundreds of patients on the upper floors using these moribund lifts. In any case, using lifts during a fire is dangerous (the lift wells act like chimneys), but how on earth would you get everyone out of the building without doing so? There are stairs, but these are hard to find and many of the patients are bed-bound and would be unable to walk down them anyway. As a producer at the BBC, I have had to attend numerous safety courses, and if the dire warnings I have listened to are correct then the Royal Free, with its cluttered corridors, overcrowded but indispensable lifts and unreliable electrics, ought to send the Health and Safety Executive into apoplexy. The problems are shared with other high-rise hospitals, but then, as the public is coming increasingly to realize, hospitals are perhaps less safe, and certainly less healthy, than we generally care to admit.

Of course, it does not have to be like this. Shortly after her tumour is diagnosed but before her operation, Anna obtains a referral through our GP to see a homoeopathic doctor who specializes in cancer care. The appointment is at St Charles' Hospital in North Kensington, and the clinic takes place in a separate annexe within the hospital grounds. We enter this building and discover a brightly-lit interior painted in bold but tasteful primary colours. The floor is carpeted, and the windows are framed by elegant yellow and blue check curtains. The furniture is modern with an abundance of natural wood. Soothing music isn't playing, but it might well be, such is the mood of lightness and calm.

It only takes us a few minutes to work out the reason for this uncharacteristically sympathetic décor: this is a 'hospice wing' for the terminally ill. And so I learn for the first time what I have since come to regard as a commonplace – that when you are dying the Health Service treats you like a human being. Sadly, up until that point, when it still might make a difference to your "outcome", you tend to be regarded as a case to be processed, apparently oblivious to your environment and everything else except the mechanics of your "cure".

At the Royal Free, the wood-covered floors and brightly-framed prints of the rooms for private patients in Gloucester Ward have something of the same, pleasant feel. So does the Friends' Oncology Unit on the eighth floor, where cancer patients receive chemotherapy treatment in an airy atmosphere of spacious calm. The treatment room enjoys magnificent views south across London; the furniture is comfortable and well upholstered; the décor fresh and flooded with natural light.

Sadly, these virtues do not extend to the hospital's main Oncology Department on the ground floor. Although the staff are comparably caring and considerate, here there are no windows, only narrow, crowded corridors, poky, misshapen consulting rooms and a heavy atmosphere of gloom. No plants or flowers could grow here, but this is where many people have to contend with devastating news about their condition and fight to retain their battered equilibrium.

Sir Christopher Wren, arguably Britain's greatest ever architect, designed two hospitals in the course of his career. Both of these beautiful buildings – the Royal Hospital, Chelsea and the Royal Naval Hospital in Greenwich – are still standing after more than 300 years, although the Naval Hospital was turned into the home of the Royal Naval College in 1869. It is hard to imagine that the present Royal Free building, or most other hospitals constructed in the last 50 years, will still be standing in 300 years time. Having spent over 125 years of its existence in a converted barracks, the Royal Free is now housed in the first hospital building to be designed with the aid of a computer. For the sake of those hospitals now under construction, one can only hope that the software has improved in the past 30 years, but the evidence suggests not. The new Royal Infirmary in Edinburgh, for instance, which opened in 2003, is characterized by windowless offices for most of the doctors, and has no kitchens – with the result that food has to be shipped in daily from outside.

The sad fact is that the finest British architects of our own era – Norman Foster, say, or Richard Rogers – have not been commissioned to design hospitals. What world-class architects have turned their hands to in terms of medical buildings in this country are – predictably, perhaps, because of their links with the dying – cancer centres. The Maggie Centre in Dundee, which offers support to cancer sufferers and their families and won the Royal Fine Art Commission's Building of the Year Award in 2004, was designed by Frank Gehry, whose other work includes the celebrated Guggenheim Museum in Bilbao. Further Maggie Centres under development include buildings in Cambridge and London, which have been designed by Daniel Libeskind (who won the commission to re-develop Ground Zero after the destruction of 9/11) and Richard Rogers (architect of the Lloyds Building in London and the Pompidou Centre in Paris).

Apparently, recent research has shown that buildings affect health, and – surprise, surprise – patients recover faster in more congenial surroundings. Natural light, low noise levels and the presence of greenery all have an effect on the stress hormones that slow healing and increase the perception of pain. The trend in hospital architecture is therefore away from the ubiquitous and monolithic "factory" or office building represented by the Royal Free (whose garden brings scant benefit since it is invisible to, and generally unused by, the hospital's occupants); and towards the hospital "campus" or "village", which incorporates green spaces in a series of discrete, low-rise structures designed to be more human in scale and less crowded.

Ironically, this is a reversion to the dominant style of hospital design in the late 19th century, when newly-built institutions tended to be composed of numerous separate "pavilions" in an attempt to ensure adequate ventilation and prevent the spread of infection. The Johns Hopkins Hospital in Baltimore, for instance, which was built from 1877 onwards, incorporated no less than 17 interconnecting structures. It was only with the general acceptance of the germ theory of disease that fresh air came to be seen as less important than disinfectants and patient isolation in preventing contagion, and architects responded to the constraints of limited urban space by abandoning pavilion-type hospitals and designing vertically expanded monoblocks. In these, the separate spaces for medical wards, laboratories, domestic facilities, administrative offices and accommodation for staff on-call were now stacked on top of one another. The basic pattern was a cross-shaped, steel-supported structure, upwards of six storeys high, with the wings connected to a central core or tower containing stairs and lifts. This has now become the model for hospitals throughout the world, making them seemingly interchangeable in their efficient but depersonalised convenience.

While the desire to create new buildings that induce a greater sense of well-being among patients and staff is therefore a welcome development, it perhaps has limited relevance to city hospitals occupying precious locations such as the Royal Free. It may be that the current crop of privately-financed "superhospitals" – like the recently-completed University College Hospital in neighbouring Euston with its 18 storeys of gleaming steel and glass – are the last of the dinosaurs. But in the absence of any easy alternative, the Royal Free just keeps on growing, with a £50m development programme currently adding new buildings to the site as well as upgrading existing facilities. Its vast concrete surfaces may be dirty, decaying and outmoded, but there is no sign at present of their imminent extinction.

CHAPTER
7

ITU TO HIV

"MARLOW: (*Interrupting*) Do you know how long I have been
   in here, in this bed? Three months. Guess what you do over
   that sort of period flat on your back.
NICOLA: Go off your head?
MARLOW: (*Bitterly*) You *think*.
NICOLA: Yes. But – about what?
MARLOW: About *everything*.
NICOLA: Yes. But –
   She stops.
MARLOW: (*Jeeringly*) But what?
NICOLA: But can you think straight? In here, I mean. Like this.
MARLOW: Oh. I mildly hallucinate now and then – But that's
   a perspective, too."

DENNIS POTTER The Singing Detective

How do you celebrate your 48th birthday? By the time you reach this
age the meals out, trips to the theatre, even birthday parties start to
merge into one another and lack vividness or particularity. But for me
this particular anniversary proves to be a decidedly unusual and

memorable occasion. After spending most of the day quietly in my hospital bed, opening a few presents that friends and family have brought in, I round it off by being wheeled away to the Royal Free's Intensive Therapy Unit (ITU).

It is Sunday, ten days after the operation on my bowel, and since that took place I have suffered a number of setbacks and disappointments. When removing the tumour, Mr Thomas decided to create an ileostomy to allow the re-sectioned colon to heal more easily, but this is not working properly. I have been back into X-ray in an attempt to diagnose the problem, and also undergone a curious and mildly uncomfortable procedure during which a radiologist attempted to "enclose" some of the internal tissue. Now my temperature is soaring, and I am growing increasingly anxious about how much longer I can cope with my massively racing heartbeat. It is something of a relief when the nurse from ITU tells me that they have a bed free and that I am to be taken there for further treatment.

"Intensive Care", or ITU, is a secluded, cocoon-like place with severely restricted access. Staff are admitted through a small door that requires a combination lock to open it. Visitors have to ring a buzzer and are then escorted to a bleak waiting room where they are kept – sometimes for long periods – before being allowed to see their ailing relative or friend. The patients themselves enter prostrate on their beds down a cluttered corridor that leads into an unexpectedly large, slightly warren-like space characterized by dim lights, hushed voices and an atmosphere (certainly compared with the rest of the hospital) of ostensible calm.

Unlike their counterparts on the regular wards, the nurses are all dressed in V-neck smocks and matching cotton trousers that are coloured pale green or light blue and more commonly seen on operating theatre staff. It gives them an appearance of being "stripped for action", an aura of cool and clinical efficiency that is matched by the quiet, authoritative manner in which they go about their tasks.

Despite the mood of unruffled purpose and calm control, ITU is a strange and mildly disturbing environment, particularly for the patients whose perceptions are distorted both by being desperately ill and by the drugs that they are given. Perhaps fortunately, I later have no personal recollection of shouting at the Orcs whom I believe are coming through the window to attack me (I have seen the film of *The*

Lord of the Rings a few weeks before). Nor can I recall telling a nurse in all seriousness about my red flying car. But these, apparently, are among the hallucinations I experience as a result of the mind-altering medication I receive. Even the memories I shall retain of my six weeks in ITU will have a distant, fractured and dream-like quality, leaving me to wonder whether the events really happened at all.

I spend my first evening in this alien, disjointed world having a line inserted in my neck through which I can be fed, and fluids, drugs or blood administered. All ITU patients are also hooked up to a screen above their beds on which their heart-rate, blood pressure and other vital indications are displayed. The staff thus have a constant visual measure of your condition, but since the screen is behind your head you remain in blissful ignorance of quite how grave that condition is.

For most of my time in ITU, I am cared for in a large room with numerous other beds, but the arrangement of curtains means that my field of vision is restricted. To my left I can see only the bed that is diagonally opposite. This is occupied by a number of different patients, but the only one I can remember later is a young man whom I think was involved in a motor-bike crash. He is unconscious, has a leg in plaster, and his head and torso are covered in bandages. He seems to have two girlfriends who regularly sit with him, but receives no other visitors. I suppose with hindsight that one of the girls might have been his sister, but I am struck at the time by the surprising lack of rancour between the two women.

Directly in front of me is a single room, though I do not recall any patients ever passing in or out of it. It is clearly occupied, however, since one day my young nurse tells me that the patient's relatives are about to be given some bad news, and that she wants to see how this is done. Rather gruesomely, it seems to me, she then slips away into this private chamber where a group of visitors and staff have already assembled.

In front of the room a passageway leads off to the right, and this is from where my visitors (strictly no more than two at a time) periodically hove into view. I am later moved to a single room further down this corridor from which I am able to see the hospital's research laboratories. This is welcome after the windowless confinement of the main ward, but to my disappointment the labs are curiously deserted of people at all times of the day or night.

On the wall of the passageway is a light-box on which the doctors hang patients' X-rays and then discuss their significance in subdued, sombre tones. After they have gone, I peer into the middle-distance wondering whether the white-filled lungs left illuminated on the screen might be my own; but my interest rapidly wanes and I soon just want the irritatingly bright light to be switched off. Shortly after admission to ITU, I contract pneumonia. To treat this I now have a hole drilled through my ribs into which a tube is inserted to drain my infected lung. Strangely, I find this less painful than a daily procedure I have to endure with the physiotherapists that involves passing a suction pipe down the back of my throat, into which I must try to cough up phlegm.

Perpendicularly to the right of my bed is a corner bay where a large man of around 60 lies in a coma. His wife comes in from time to time and talks to him in an awful, droning voice that cuts through the quiet and calm like a grating stone. "George…George. It's Marie. I hope you can hear me George. I went down to the market today. Had to do the shopping. George? Sally's coming over later. She sends her love, George." I desperately wish that she would shut up, and remember having the unkind thought that George is probably staying in his coma deliberately – anything to avoid his wife's annoying prattle. It is a salutary experience later when a friend – whom I had no idea had come to visit when I was unconscious myself for several days – tells me how difficult and strange it was trying to talk to me in my comatose state.

My time is mostly passed in a slightly troubled haze. With no windows to let in the daylight, no meals to break the monotony (everyone is drip-fed), and with me and all the other patients drifting in and out of sleep or consciousness on an irregular basis, there are no markers against which to chart the passage of time. Doctors loom up in front of me from time to time and discuss what to do next, but there seems to be no pattern to these appearances. The days drift into one another in a blur of constantly-lit other-worldliness. Neither day nor night, an uncomfortable waking dream or low-level nightmare in which all divisions seem to fade and melt, and all order seems random. The only regular event is the nurses' change of shift.

I imagine at one time that I have been moved to Manchester. At another that I am in a basement which is still part of the Royal Free complex on the Ealing Road in Alperton. In fact the only place I go is by portable crane to a chair beside my bed. This involves being strapped into a sky-blue harness, which is like a huge nappy made of toughened plastic, and then winched off the bed and swung onto the seat. I find it a distressing and humiliating experience rather than a liberating one. Later I learn to use my legs again using a zimmer frame in one of the corridors.

After I first recover consciousness and am taken off the ventilator that has kept me breathing, the staff are concerned that the machine may have damaged my vocal chords. So one of the nurses encourages me to exercise them by singing. He sits down beside me on the bed and then trips lightly up and down the scale. "La-la-la-la-la-la-la-la-la." The sonorous notes sound strange in the muted calm that envelops us. "Now, you," he says. After a few moments my cracked and croaky voice weakly follows his. "La-la-la-la-la-la-la-la-la." A discordant but audible cry of life. I have become not the Singing Detective, but the Singing Patient.

When the doctors consider me ready to leave ITU for the first time (I actually spend two separate periods there with a few days on a regular ward in between), I am transferred to the "step-down" unit. Here a rather glamorous, middle-eastern looking woman with a mass of curly, dark brown hair lies propped on a huge bank of pillows. The curtains around her bed float hypnotically, wafted by breezes from the fans that are being used to keep her cool. For some reason I believe this room with its unexpected occupant to be high up in the trees in a rural location on the edge of London somewhere off the A40.

One evening before that (at least I think it was an evening) the nurse who has been looking after me comes to the foot of my bed towards the end of his shift seeming decidedly anxious and ill at ease. He is a young, short-haired Australian, and is accompanied by a senior female colleague who begins, equally uncomfortably, to tell me that they have a problem. Apparently, my nurse has accidentally managed to cut himself while performing some procedure in which my blood was also involved. (It is a measure of how far detached I am from reality at this time that I now have absolutely no idea what this procedure might have been.) Anyway, as a result my blood could have infected his, and they are therefore wondering whether I might be prepared to have an HIV test to see if he is now at risk from AIDS. Even in my hazy state, I remember feeling slightly bemused by this bizarre request, as well as finding something more than a little comic in the extreme seriousness with which it is delivered. I say it isn't a problem and that they are welcome to do the test.

However, having secured my agreement, hospital protocol now clearly requires that I should be given counselling about the possible consequences. So the senior nurse promptly launches into a long preamble about whether I realize what a "positive" result (an odd choice of words in the context) will mean. An HIV test I am happy to undergo, but a protracted advice and therapy session is another matter. I interrupt and say that having been monogamous for the past 20 years, which, as far as I know, my wife has also been, I think it pretty unlikely that I have AIDS, and that this is not therefore a major anxiety to me. I could add that since I am already at death's door it doesn't currently seem to matter a great deal whether I am HIV-positive or not. But there is no need. My curt intervention appears to do the trick, and I am soon left to rest in peace.

Ironically, in view of all this up-front concern, I am never actually given the result of my test (or if I am I have no memory of it). However, my anxious Australian nurse appears on duty a few days later looking mightily relieved, and immediately comes over to my bed, shakes me by the hand and says "thank you". He never specifies for what exactly, but I take it to mean that the test has come back negative.

CHAPTER
8

FALLING

"Either the well was very deep, or she fell very slowly, for she
had plenty of time as she went down to look about her, and to
wonder what was going to happen next."
LEWIS CARROLL Alice's Adventures in Wonderland

I think it is Saturday morning. I awake quite early and for some reason
want to sit on the side of my bed. The nurse isn't happy about it, but I
stubbornly persist. I should listen to what she is saying. A few moments
later, glazed and unaware, I fall off my bed.

I come round to find myself flat on my back on the bed again, with
a host of anxious faces staring down at me. It isn't an unpleasant feeling to be receiving so much attention, and I gradually work out what
has happened. I have seen the panic on the ward that ensues when the
emergency "crash" button is pressed, and all the medical staff race to
help the poor victim. This time the cause of anxiety is me.

Karen, the young Irish nurse who has obviously scooped me off the
floor and back onto the bed, continues to hold me as the other staff
gradually drift away, happy that I am all right. "You had us worried
there," she says, her face still full of concern. I feel quite clear-headed

and am a bit bemused by all the fuss. But, with hindsight, it is the first indication that I am still seriously unwell.

■ ■ ■

A couple of weeks later I come round again in Intensive Care to find Anna and my younger brother, Nigel, looking down at me. Nigel is smiling, almost ecstatically, and talks about me being a fighter, a hero. Anna is more subdued and tells me not to worry about the day or time as I have "lost" two or three days.

■ ■ ■

As I begin to recover, I am repeatedly frustrated by seeming to make progress only for some development to occur that sweeps me backwards to where I was some time before. "I keep falling off my bike," I complain to my friend, Colin Luke. Hardly surprising perhaps for someone who can't even stay on his bed. "Just remember to keep pedalling," Colin advises.

■ ■ ■

During my time in Intensive Care, I have a curious and repeated waking dream of "floating" through the air on my back, buoyed up by strange, thermal-like breezes. This seems to take place in a sort of Umbrian hill-top village, and is quite an exhilarating sensation. I am defying gravity, but feel quite safe. I have no recollection of landing, but clearly that presents no problem.

■ ■ ■

There is the most wonderful autumn in the months after I am discharged from the Royal Free. Fantastic colours – browns, greens, rusts and yellows. I spend many happy hours watching the leaves fall from the trees in our garden. I notice that they come down rather faster than I had imagined, often spinning as they make their way earthwards. The effect is always graceful though, and the landing soft.

■ ■ ■

Autumn or "Fall" always used to be my favourite season when I was a student. One of my happier memories of Cambridge is cycling across the Backs in the fresh morning air, admiring the beauty of the trees as they blended seamlessly with the glorious stone and architecture of the college buildings. I also recollect reciting Keats' ode "To Autumn" with Anna when our relationship was first beginning, coming home one sunny September morning after a party the night before. I still love the colours of autumn, but these days prefer the expectant coolness of spring and summer mornings to autumn ones. A sign of ageing, I fear, although I look back with gentle amusement at my youthful, romantic self.

■ ■ ■

Am I scared of "falling" now? And by that do I mean dying? I think the answer to both questions is probably "yes". Too much to hold on for. "Keep pedalling," I tell myself. It is a long time now since I fell off my bed.

CHAPTER
9

FICTIONS

"The times are strange enough. Why make things up?"
IAN McEWAN Saturday

Despite the contemporaneity of the rise of the novel and the emergence of the modern "clinical" hospital – developments which the French thinker Michel Foucault would argue are not unrelated, both being bound up with the blossoming discipline during the 18th century of detailed and recorded observation – there is little hospital-inspired literature. Try to think of a great hospital novel. (Try to name any novel which is predominantly set in a hospital come to that.) Aleksandr Solzhenitsyn's *Cancer Ward* is the best I can come up with, the encompassing humanity of which has an enduring power that transcends the political controversy which accompanied its original publication. If you stretch the definition of hospital to include TB sanatoria and mental institutions, then Thomas Mann's *The Magic Mountain* or Ken Kesey's *One Flew Over the Cuckoo's Nest* might also lay claim to consideration, but what is generally noteworthy is how seldom hospitals feature in serious prose fiction.

Doctors are well represented, with a range of characters that stretches from Tertius Lydgate in *Middlemarch* and Allan Woodcourt in *Bleak House* through Charles Bovary and the eponymous Dr Jekyll to Dick Diver in Scott Fitzgerald's *Tender is the Night* and Tomas, the hero of Milan Kundera's *The Unbearable Lightness of Being*. But only the last of these is hospital-based, and the hospital features in the book not as a major narrative setting, but merely as a place of employment where Tomas loses his job for political reasons, forcing him to find work as a GP. Hospitals are surprisingly rare in the literary landscape, and where they do appear – in John Wyndham's *The Day of the Triffids*, for instance, or Martin Amis's *Other People* – it often tends to be as an ostensible place of safety where you awake into nightmare, but which the protagonist must leave in order for that nightmare to be confronted and the adventure proper to begin.

It may be that the static quality of hospitals, and the enclosed nature of the characters and stories to be found there, are an inhibition to prose narrative. But it is precisely these characteristics, together with the unity of place that follows from them, which make hospitals a wonderfully fertile location for drama.

Historically, there are a number of intriguing links between the worlds of medicine and drama. The most celebrated surviving theatre from the ancient world at Epidaurus in Greece – on which the Olivier auditorium in our own National Theatre is modelled – is situated within a sanctuary to Asklepios, the Greek god of healing. Asklepios is often portrayed with his daughters Hygeia (health) and Panacea (cure-all), and his sons supposedly became the first physicians. The site at Epidaurus contains not just a theatre, but also a temple dedicated to the god and *enkoimeteria* (sleeping areas) for the sick. These were, in some sense, the first hospital wards, and of those who slept there some would be cured after their slumbers, others would have the treatment they should follow revealed to them in dreams, and those less fortunate would leave having experienced no reverie, which was considered a bad omen for the course of their illness. From earliest times, healing and drama seem to have belonged together.

During the 19th century, the brilliant French physiologist Claude Bernard made a host of remarkable discoveries concerning "homoeostasis" – the mechanisms by which the body balances the interdependent elements that compose it to maintain a constant "internal environment". This led to him being awarded a Chair at the

Sorbonne, a seat in the Senate and the presidency of the French Academy. Yet he only took up medicine after he had failed in his original dream of becoming a dramatist.

When New End Hospital in Hampstead became part of the Royal Free in 1968, its mortuary was subsequently converted into the New End Theatre, which continues to present small-scale professional productions to this day. Given the links between hospitals and the stage (think of the very term "operating theatre"), it is perhaps no surprise that one of the consultants at the Royal Free, Professor Winslet, is alleged to be a cousin of Kate, the award-winning film actress. He certainly revealed thespian tendencies of his own on the hospital's 175th anniversary when he played its founder, William Marsden, in a pageant to mark the event. My closest friend was treated recently at St George's Hospital in Tooting by Mr Fiennes, a consultant surgeon who is reputed to belong to the acting dynasty that boasts Ralph and Joseph among its scions.

Whether it is some deep-seated link between the two professions or merely the effect of ward rounds being a kind of public performance, there is a pronounced theatricality about the manner of many hospital consultants. On a less exalted plane, I once spent a strangely diverting day in ITU watching a grotesquely self-regarding registrar as he hectored and bullied the extremely pretty nurse who was looking after me, and then proceeded to ask her out for a post-work drink as her shift drew towards its conclusion. When she declined, he simply turned his attentions to another unfortunate female, behaving throughout with the exaggerated emotions of some bad actor in a third-rate episode of *Casualty*. His manner seemed like a poor imitation of how he thought doctors are supposed to behave.

This is instructive, since undoubtedly it is on screen that the role models for all forms of medical behaviour and practice are now to be found. Over the past 40 years, there have been a number of successful stage plays set in hospitals, such as Peter Nichols' *The National Health* and Brian Clark's *Whose Life Is It Anyway?* But significantly both these plays were first written for television (in the case of *The National Health* as a drama entitled *The End Beds*), for it is in the cinema and latterly on the small screen that hospital drama has found its true home.

The successful series of Doctor Kildare films in America during the

1930s was followed by the hugely popular *Doctor in the House* in Britain in the 1950s. This in turn spawned a host of cinematic sequels and – like *Dr Kildare* – a subsequent hit TV series. Interestingly, both these long-running successes started life as a series of novels – by Max Brand and Richard Gordon respectively – but it was only when they were translated into screen dramas that they achieved their iconic status in the popular imagination.

In 1957 Granada Television launched *Emergency – Ward 10*, Britain's first twice-weekly drama serial, which ran for ten years and created the prototype for the relentless barrage of hospital dramas that now crowds our TV screens. From *Casualty* and *Holby City* on the BBC to ITV's copycat emergency drama *Always and Everyone* and the updating of the 1970s' nurses' drama *Angels* in the form of Channel 4's imaginatively entitled *No Angels*, long-running hospital "soaps" have become one of the staple ingredients of British television production. And when the supply of domestic series runs out, there is a host of American imports to fall back on. The tradition of *Dr Kildare* contin-ues with hardy perennials such as *ER* and *St Elsewhere*, and more recent hits such as *Scrubs, Grey's Anatomy* and *House*. For the hospital drama addict, there are programmes available at least two or three times a week, and in peak seasons seemingly every night.

When I was working in the BBC's TV Drama Department in the early 1990s and *Casualty* was at the height of its success, the demand was constantly being made to find more "precinct dramas". The com-bination of cheapness, brought about by concentrating the action in a single location (which in the case of *Casualty* was a set housed in an industrial warehouse rather than in an expensive purpose-built studio), together with huge and appreciative audiences was more than the programme commissioners could resist. With the movement of the camera compensating for the static setting and frequently bed-bound protagonists, and with multiple narratives adding even more urgency to stories that were naturally matters of life and death anyway, hospi-tal drama had found a winning formula. However, it was not one which translated easily to other environments. The offshoot of *Casualty*'s success was not a burgeoning of precinct dramas, merely more hospital ones.

As a result, it is now from television that our idea of hospitals is mostly derived. But what form does it take? What image of hospitals does the plethora of small-screen dramas collectively perpetrate? How do they shape our thinking and affect our expectations of what hospitals are like? Obviously portrayals vary, but if one looks for common characteristics across the range of output, the first and most striking impression is of how busy the contemporary hospital is.

In part this reflects the producers' wish to create high-pressured and compelling drama. When *Casualty* started, each episode crammed no fewer than five separate storylines into its 50 minutes, quite apart from ongoing events in the lives of the regular characters. This kind of narrative density has since become the norm for hospital drama. Deficiencies of emotional intensity and dramatic realization in any given plot-line are simply brushed over by the sheer weight of event, as the action cuts rapidly from one case to the next. But although there is an artistic imperative governing this, it is also true to life. Modern hospitals are busy places that hum with people and activity, even if, mercifully, their wards are not quite the manic arenas of senselessly milling extras found in *Holby City*. This surfeit of background action is partly compensation for a pragmatic culling of foreground players – large surgical "firms" stalking the wards and having case discussions in which everyone speaks are vastly more expensive than having mute trolley-pushers drift through shot, so consultants tend unrealistically to hunt alone in this environment. However, the impression it creates definitely has a basis in reality. Significantly, the nostalgic BBC medical series *Born and Bred*, set in the years following the Second World War, revolves around a tiny cottage hospital that is run almost as a sideline by the local GPs, who initially even seek to keep its existence a secret from the newly-formed NHS. It is as if the friendly, tranquil and often deserted hospital could not possibly survive contact with the bureaucratic juggernaut of a state-run health system, and can now only exist as a Sunday night dream from a vanished world – a mythical embodiment of all that contemporary hospitals are not. The dream has next to no basis in historical truth.

Yet although the hospital environment of contemporary television dramas may be uncomfortably cluttered and frantic, the staff who inhabit it are for the most part undeniably heroic, in line with the general pattern of modern TV heroes. That is to say that, like their counterparts in police or other dramas, they are personally flawed but professionally magnificent. Hugh Laurie as the maverick, disabled genius in *House* is but a variation on Robbie Coltrane's combative, self-destructive but inspired Fitz in *Cracker*. There is a similar line that links the driven, wilful talent of Jane Tennison in *Prime Suspect* to the arrogant but gifted Connie Beauchamp in *Holby City*. Whatever their personal shortcomings, these doctors are almost never *medically* defeated. They may be frustrated by patients' stupidity or compromised by institutional constraints, they may even have to struggle with complications thrown up by their own messy emotional lives. But despite their being constantly embattled, illness alone routinely buckles in the face of their professional prowess. In this they offer a somewhat glamourized and rose-tinted view of hospital doctors, who in real life are rather more inclined to remain baffled by the cases that confront them, less likely always to come through with the brilliantly-conceived diagnosis or unconventional life-saving treatment. On the other hand, real doctors in my experience show greater – and more appropriate – professional detachment. They also speak in fewer clichés.

If doctors are generally portrayed as overwhelmingly talented in hospital drama, then patients are subject to a comparable distortion as most of them seem to make lightning recoveries and experience little or no pain. While pain control has rightly become a high priority in contemporary hospital medicine (the Royal Free even has a specialist team devoted to its pursuit), most patients – particularly post-surgical ones – are still in various states of discomfort and distress. This constant feeling of affliction – where all movement is difficult and hour upon hour is passed in low-level torments of aching, nausea, exhaustion and irritability – bears no relation to the momentary grimaces of agony that seem to be the limit of most television characters' suffering. After one of my major abdominal operations, I was kept on an epidural for several days to relieve the pain. However, for some reason (possibly my massively reduced body weight), the effects of this localized anaesthetic wore off extremely quickly once the painkiller stopped being infused into my system; and hospital protocol dictated that the nurses could not be issued with a replacement bottle of the epidural drug until the previous one was finished. The result was that during the hour or more that it took for my nurse to realize that the bottle was empty, go to the pharmacy to obtain a new one and then fix it to my drip (while simultaneously attending to several other patients), I was in acute pain. Not of the sharp, stabbing, scream-out-loud variety – the brief spasm permitted to TV patients when unconsciousness is considered dramatically inappropriate – but an all-consuming, twist-and-turn-to-try-and-escape-it agony, in which meaningful conversation or any other activity is rendered completely impossible. All I could think about was my discomfort. In an extreme form, this is the lot of many hospital patients for much of the time. It is the opposite of dramatic – there is no development or crisis and it blights all engagement with other people. Perhaps not surprisingly, therefore, it never seems to feature in hospital drama.

A further aspect of how little effect illness or treatment seems to have on television patients is the miraculous speed of their recoveries after surgery. I remember visiting Anna for the first time a few hours after her cancer operation. She was in a half-sleep, with a gastric tube up her nose and an oxygen mask over her face. It was as much as she could do to open her eyes and make a wan half-smile. Conversation was unthinkable. Her response to my enquiry as to how she was consisted of murmurs and single words. Yet patients recovering from major surgery on television seem able to conduct life-changing dialogues with their partners within moments of coming round. Modern anaesthetics are less debilitating and long-lasting than they were 20 or 30 years ago, but I have been groggy and incommunicative for hours after procedures that only involved brief sedation, never mind hours of complete unconsciousness.

Hospital dramas gorge themselves on the crises and extreme, life-changing situations that illness provokes, but they have comparatively little interest in illness itself and the accurate portrayal of its treatment. The demands of narrative "closure" (a host of stories to be wrapped up each week with only the running "soap" of the ongoing characters' lives to be left hanging for the next episode) mean that cases are resolved with enviable rapidity and finality. The illness *is* diagnosed, the operation *is* performed and the patient *will* get better. The ongoing messiness of the real world, where treatments often do not work immediately or produce lingering complications and undesirable side effects, is not the stuff of long-running TV series. My own story – of still inching my way towards recovery some four years after my "crisis" in Intensive Care – has no place in the small screen's depiction of illness. On television I would simply have got better or died, no cloudy half-measures.

In part this reflects the precinct quality of the television hospital, its detachment from the outside world. Stories, like the building, are self-contained. The outside world, if featured at all, is where accidents occur that need to be treated; the place from which patients arrive with their problems (physical or emotional) needing cures – that our heroes generally provide. There is seldom much interplay between the hospital and society at large, no real impact felt of political target-setting on hospital practice and morale, or of local property prices on staffing levels. Financial constraints, operational problems with IT systems, transport difficulties affecting patients and shift-workers: these rarely achieve any plot significance. In any continuing series, the drama soon becomes focused on the lives and emotions of its running characters. Even the medicine tends to be trivialized and contained – a shot of narrative intensity that can be turned on and off like a tap.

If our idea of hospitals is thus of places at one remove from the outside world, this distinctness can take two forms. Either it is highly stylized, or it is exaggeratedly, almost excessively, "real". The artificially-lit, stage-set world of the Royal Free's Casualty Department has its fictional equivalent in the clinical white light, stripped-out décor and icy-blue colours of the A & E set in *Always and Everywhere*. No murky earth shades or messily-dressed flotsam off the streets are to be found here. Everything is pristine and pure. American hospital dramas also seem generally to be set in far more stylish and tasteful environments than their British counterparts. This may reflect the greater wealth of American institutions, and actually be more realistic than it appears to us on the other side of the Atlantic. But the moody, atmospheric lighting, sleek furnishings and carefully controlled colours of *ER* or *House* still clearly mark off the hospitals in which they are set as separate, art-directed worlds, as enclosed and artificial environments.

The contrast with *Casualty*, or even *Holby City*, could not be greater. Here the lighting is flat and murky: stark, hospital neon; the colours are dirty; and the frame is clogged with people, all shot up close with little fluidity and an uncompromising relish for mess and gore. At first sight this is the "truth" about hospitals – the brutal, unvarnished reality of the night shift (on which *Casualty* was originally set) in a busy, urban A & E Department. And yet my experience of the Royal Free was less *Casualty* than *The Singing Detective*.

For although the world of *Casualty* seems more connected to the everyday world we inhabit, it is still only a partial reality that the series describes. Its stark naturalism affords little place to dirty toilets, decaying city infrastructures or the implications of the drift towards private financing on public institutions. (In its early years the programme did endeavour to reflect wider social issues such as these, but it is hard to imagine Cabinet Ministers attacking the series now as anti-government as they did in the late 1980s.) The series – like all long-running medical dramas – also depicts the hospital very much from a staff point of view.

The genius of *The Singing Detective* – perhaps the finest of all television hospital dramas and one of the finest television dramas, full stop – is that it captures, in all its bewildering variety, the patient's perspective. Dennis Potter's distillation of his many years of treatment reflects with burning intensity the "Wonderland" of the hospital world. As it drifts between remembered scenes of childhood, the cheap paperback fantasies of a B-movie thriller, and vivid, grotesque fragments of one man's day-to-day experience in a crowded hospital ward, the serial brings to life the strange, dream-like quality of the enclosed hospital environment that most dramas ignore. The grim and surreal humour, the curious shifts of perspective and disjointed succession of events, the uncertain boundaries between what is objectively real and what takes place only inside your head: these elements of what you experience as a patient are excluded as much from *Casualty* as from more stylised television dramas, but they are as much part of the hospital world as broken limbs and blood. It is Potter's distinction to have put them on screen and to make them part of our imaginative frame of reference.

There are interesting developments of the idea of the hospital that television has largely created in two powerful recent novels. Ian McEwan's *Saturday* follows a day in the life of a neurosurgeon who works at University College Hospital in central London. Viewed from his perspective, the hospital – and particularly the operating theatre on which his personal fiefdom is centred – is a reassuring microcosm of order. It offers a welcome haven of clear, ethical imperatives and calm, rational, life-giving activity in contrast to the confused morality, uneasy tensions and destructive violence of the world outside. Although more controlled, this corresponds to the separate, self-contained settings of most fictional hospitals on television, which are also conceived from a staff point of view. However, it bears little relation to many – perhaps most – patients' experience. For me, the hospital is less a bastion of order than a vision of chaos – a nightmare world where operations go wrong, where causes – never mind cures – are uncertain, where desperate people compete for attention and are often treated with less than benign consideration. It seems not a comfortable retreat from the troubled realm outside, but a terrifying prison from which one is desperate to escape.

Tim Parks' *Destiny* explores the world of hospitals from the point of view of an agonized journalist who visits three of them – all in Italy – in the course of the narrative, as he goes in search of his dead son's body following the boy's suicide. The hospital in this book is one of several antiseptic "non-places" against which the story is set. It sits alongside the characterless hotel foyer, the airport waiting lounge and the express train carriage as a place of transit, a bland and slightly inhuman context the anonymous indifference of which is in stark contrast to the passionate turmoil of the central character's mind. At one point he reflects on the contrast between airports and hospitals:

> "Airports the world over I couldn't help thinking as we
> hurriedly followed the orderly's directions, are the same
> kaleidoscope of neon and consumer goods while hospitals the
> world over…are a dingy, under-funded maze of linoleum
> corridors, grey screens, white coats and peremptory warnings."

But as he goes on to describe the bolted-together plastic seats and neon lighting of the Turin *policlinico*, it is the faceless similarity of the two environments that actually emerges.

What the novel captures is the dislocation or alienation of the hospital visitor – a perspective also to be found in Alan Bennett's novella *Father! Father! Burning Bright* (which is, incidentally and perhaps predictably, a spin-off from his 1982 television play *Intensive Care*). Engulfed by powerful emotions, the grieving relative in both stories feels an outsider at the bedside – someone who experiences a disturbing lack of connection with the relentless, steady rhythm of the hospital routine. While this seeming obliviousness of the institution to the upset and distress of those within its walls comes closer to my own experience, I personally have found that the hospital exists in a continuum with the chaos of my inner world, rather than occupying a space in contrast to it: uncaring and unfeeling perhaps, but no more ordered or controlled.

Of course all these imaginative visions have their own validity, but cumulatively they add up to a received image of hospitals as, at worst, busy and impersonal factories – large and rather crowded non-places, a bit like a badly funded airport. However, they are staffed by brilliant, heroic physicians, and bodily pain or mental confusion have no real place here. Medical crises may occasionally result in a swift death, but they are invariably resolved with complete finality and enviable rapidity. The hospital we don't see – and therefore don't carry with us as part of our expectations – is the chaotic Babel, the stifling prison where hope is bled dry, the shadow world of nightmare, the terrifying Wonderland where miraculous cures can all too readily turn into the ashes of long-term suffering and despair. It is a significant – and in many ways a dangerous – omission.

CHAPTER
10

PRAGUE

"She went outside and set off in the direction of the embankment.
She wanted to see the Vltava. She wanted to stand on its banks and
look long and hard into its waters, because the sight of the flow was
soothing and healing. The river flowed from century to century, and
human affairs play themselves out on its banks. Play themselves out
to be forgotten the next day, while the river flows on.

Leaning against the balustrade, she peered into the water. She
was on the outskirts of Prague, and the Vltava had already flowed
through the city, leaving behind the glory of the Castle and
churches; like an actress after a performance, it was tired and
contemplative; it flowed on between its dirty banks, bounded by
walls and fences that themselves bounded factories and abandoned
playgrounds."

MILAN KUNDERA The Unbearable Lightness of Being

I first visited Prague in the spring of 1999. We were staying with relatives in Krakow, southern Poland, for Easter and decided to take
couchettes on an overnight train to the Czech capital for a few days'

sightseeing there. Anna, our two young sons and I arrived at Prague's main railway station at 6am, and immediately made our way through the chill, early-morning gloom to Wenceslas Square. There were flowers on the spot where Jan Palach had set fire to himself in 1969 in protest at the Soviet invasion, but otherwise few signs of life. When we reached the Hotel Europa, its beautiful art deco restaurant, where we planned to eat breakfast, was still closed. So we continued on, past the Tyl Theatre, where Mozart's *Don Giovanni* was first performed, through the old town and eventually out onto the famous King Charles Bridge across the River Vltava. It was magically deserted, and there, looming above us through the grey mist of receding dawn, I caught my first glimpse of Prague Castle. It was a magnificent sight: sombre and silent, casting its all-seeing yet somehow oblivious gaze over our tiny forms on the river and beyond us over the entire city through which we had passed.

Prague Castle is the largest castle in the world, more like a self-contained town than a mere building, with cottages, palaces, shops and even a cathedral all housed within its vast walls. The brooding way it overlooks the surrounding neighbourhood provided inspiration for Franz Kafka's great novel *The Castle*; and although the two buildings could hardly be more different architecturally, it also reminds me of the Royal Free in the way it dominates the vision of the scurrying community that nestles in its shadow. Both hospital and castle are monumental and oppressive, intrusive and hard to escape.

Curiously, the view from inside out at the Royal Free also has affinities with Prague. For much of my five-month stay in the hospital, I occupied a single room on the ninth floor. It offered magnificent vistas across the Heath in one direction and over Hampstead village in the other. I could just glimpse Keats' House in Wentworth Place where the ailing poet and former medical student fell in love with Fanny Brawne; and I spent hours watching cars draw to a halt at the zebra crossing in front of Hampstead Heath station and wait as the pedestrians crossed to catch their trains or do their shopping. But what struck me most was the way that the closely packed houses fanned out over Hampstead hill. They looked completely un-English, and recalled to my mind the cover of a book about the European Reformation that I read when I was studying A Level History. This featured a painting that depicted medieval Prague, its houses similarly "stuck on" to the hillside with a strange, two-dimensional flatness. When it unexpectedly snowed heavily in mid-March and only the brown faces of the buildings were visible amid the enshrouding whiteness, the identification was complete. As I sat lonely in my room, I felt I was no longer in England but transported to the silent, romantic grandeur of central Europe.

Having taken over 40 years to make my first visit to Prague, by a typically perverse irony I found myself travelling there a further ten or dozen times in the year that followed. On our return to England from Poland, I was invited to produce the second series of *The Scarlet Pimpernel* starring Richard E Grant for the BBC. For financial and design reasons, much of the first series had been shot in the Czech Republic, and, attracted by the prospect of spending more time in the beautiful Czech capital as well as thinking that working on a period action adventure (something I had never done before) would be fun, I agreed to the offer and took the job.

It was a huge mistake. Much of the first series had been paid for with American money, but for a host of complicated political reasons that had little to do with the programme, the American co-producers decided they did not wish to invest in the second. Together with the Executive Producer of the series, I therefore spent much of the months that followed trying to make good the budgetary shortfall, while simultaneously travelling backwards and forwards to Prague in order to set up filming for Richard E Grant's limited window of availability.

Some six weeks before shooting, a lurch to the right in the Austrian general election meant that a plan to film some of the series in Vienna, where generous financial subsidies had been on offer to foreign production companies, collapsed. The government no longer wished to stimulate inward investment, and our programme's precarious budgetary structure was thrown into crisis. The BBC still wanted the show. It simply could not afford, or did not wish, to pay for it; and, as is not unusual in such circumstances, promptly went into a mode of "corporate denial". I struggled on, vainly trying to reconcile the Channel

Controller's wish for a "James Bond in tights" with a budget more suited to a contemporary, domestic *chatfest*. But I singularly failed to persuade the raft of executives above me to address the problem – or even properly to acknowledge that there was one. Interestingly, my mounting feeling that I was being saddled with responsibility for a disastrous situation while being denied any effective power to deal with it by those who did possess that authority is a complaint shared by many doctors and other frontline workers in the NHS at this time. Eventually, after the first of three feature-length programmes had been shot, it became clear that I could not possibly deliver what the BBC desired to a standard I considered acceptable and bring the programme in on budget. So I resigned.

In the course of my work on the series, however, I had spent a great deal of time in Prague and its surrounding districts, and grown to love this magnificent and stylish city. But despite its glorious architecture, fine restaurants and mysteriously winding streets, Prague will forever be associated in my mind with the biggest nightmare of my professional career. My memories of it are painful and in some ways bitter ones.

CHAPTER
11

CHARING CROSS

"Well, well, go and play till the light fades away,
And then go home to bed."

WILLIAM BLAKE Nurse's Song

I first stayed in hospital when I was five or six years old. As a young child I suffered from painful and recurrent earaches, and to deal with the problem was taken to Charing Cross Hospital to have my adenoids removed.

I have no recollection of meeting the surgeon beforehand or of any pre-admission appointment, so my initial encounter with the hospital (which was then still in Charing Cross rather than in Fulham as, rather confusingly, it is now) was on the day of my admission.

I remember arriving bearing a small, soft-topped black suitcase, which my father later used for storing his 8mm home movies. The entrance was through a long porch made of wood and glass – rather dark and quietly sombre.

I stayed in a small children's ward up on the second or third floor, which was much lighter and airier. However, on my first night there I was disturbed and upset as I tried to sleep by a boy crying in the bed next to mine. A nurse came and comforted him. These days, of course, his mother would be allowed to stay alongside him.

Around lunchtime on the day of our operations, all the children went into the adult ward adjacent to our own and received a spoonful of drugged jam from a woman whom I thought was the Matron, though with hindsight was probably just a Sister. She sat at a table in the centre of the ward, and I remember feeling slightly frightened by the patients in the beds around, many of whom looked extremely ill and frail. The children, by comparison, all seemed in rude health. We returned to our beds and promptly fell asleep.

When I awoke, what seemed like many hours later after my operation, it was already dark. (I think it was wintertime.) A nurse came to see me, but told me it was now night-time, and that I must go back to sleep. I remember being most put out (I had just woken up), but reluctantly complied.

One of the pleasures of going into hospital was being given presents, which were normally reserved for birthdays and Christmas. I recall my father came to visit one lunchtime (he worked just up the road in Westminster), and brought me a domed plastic snow-storm. This now seems very *Citizen Kane*, and has sadly long since been lost. I was also given the two latest *Noddy* books. Numbers 19 and 20 in the series if my memory serves me correctly: *Noddy and the Bunkey* and *Noddy and the Tootles.*

I stayed in for a total of four or five days, and on the morning of my departure had an enjoyable time playing with a toy fort in a glassy gallery positioned next to our ward. It was a Sunday, grey and very quiet in the street down below. Another boy came and joined in my game. I felt rather sad when my mother arrived to take me home.

Years later, when Covent Garden was being re-developed in the mid-1970s, I turned off the Strand into Agar Street and unexpectedly came face to face with the distinctive grid-iron shape of the old hospital building. It was no longer in use as a hospital, but the gallery where I had played that Sunday morning was still clearly visible above my head, running away from the acutely angled curve of the building's façade. The sight brought memories of my stay flooding back with an almost Proustian intensity. They were not unpleasant ones – and the operation I had there did cure my earaches.

CHAPTER
12

FEAR

"'Now, my good dear Betty,' said Mrs Boffin, 'we have come to remove Johnny from this cottage to where he can be taken better care of.'

Instantly, and before another word could be spoken, the old woman started up with blazing eyes, and rushed at the door with the sick child.

'Stand away from me every one of ye!' she cried out wildly. 'I see what ye mean now. Let me go my way, all of ye. I'd sooner kill the Pretty, and kill myself!'…

But, catching sight of Mrs Boffin's wholesome face, she relented, and crouching down by the door and bending over her burden to hush it, said humbly: 'Maybe my fears has put me in the wrong. If they have so, tell me, and the good Lord forgive me! I'm quick to take this fright, I know, and my head is summ'at light with wearying and watching.'"

CHARLES DICKENS Our Mutual Friend

The fear of hospitals is profound, and has a long and vigorous tradition. In his short history of medicine, *Blood and Guts*, Roy

Porter quotes an American doctor reflecting on 50 years of practice in 1930:

> "One of the very greatest changes I have observed...has been in the attitude of the public toward hospitals. Dread of them was general and well founded before the days of antiseptic surgery. But with its widespread adoption, fear faded rapidly from the lay mind. All over the world the very name 'hospital' suggested pestilence or insanity; few people would go voluntarily to such a place, no matter how well equipped it was for doing routine work effectively. Today almost everybody with an illness at all serious wishes to go there."

My grandfather's mistrust of hospitals may have been cast against the tide of progress and this hard-won reduction of fear, but its roots lay deeper than simply his own experience. There was nothing unusual or anachronistic in my mother recently echoing his desire, when she became terminally ill, that she should be allowed to die at home. Indeed, the fact that she was able to do so was due to the support of a nursing charity specifically dedicated to creating "a hospice in the home".

Being born at a time when hospitals were perhaps approaching their peak of public regard, I did not grow up with my family's tradition of dread as part of my inheritance. But regrettably, after five months in the Royal Free, I acquired it. In the months following my discharge I felt a physical reaction down my spine at the very prospect of entering the building, even for a routine outpatient's appointment. I was terrified of being hauled back in again, of an examination being followed by a further period of incarceration. I dreaded with phobia-like intensity the very real physical discomfort that certain hospital procedures entail. The prospect of pipes once more being fed through my nostrils and into my stomach, of choking on cameras thrust into my mouth and down my oesophagus, of probes being forced up my rectum, was more than I could bear. The memory of having my face covered with a large, opaque oxygen mask that felt as if it was suffocating me made me shudder with anticipatory horror.

It is the middle of the night, not long after my first operation. I stir from my troubled slumbers to see a new patient being brought to the bed opposite mine. He is a tiny, incredibly frail-looking person of eastern origin. He says nothing, and with his diminutive frame, smooth skin and longish, swept-down hair, I actually mistake him for a woman. Shortly after his arrival, an electrically-driven mobile X-ray machine glides between our beds in sinister silence, and the nurses and radiographer set about positioning him for a chest X-ray. He is so weak he can hardly sit up unaided, but they eventually wedge him into position. Then the staff all retreat to a safe distance while the X-ray is taken, but, as that is not an option offered to me, for a few moments I have an uninterrupted view of the new arrival. Alone and lit by a single overhead bedlight, I do not believe I have ever seen anyone look quite so scared.

Strangely, when I return to the ward from Intensive Care several weeks later, I spend a single night in a shared room where this man is again one of the other patients. He is due to be discharged the following day, and is almost unrecognisable as the petrified, bulging-eyed creature of that haunting night-time vision. Gone is the look of undiluted animal terror, and in its place appears the comfortable ease of a physically transformed and much stronger-looking man, who is happily chatting to his wife and shortly to go home.

■ ■ ■

Fear in and of hospitals is composed of many elements, but sadly it seems to be on the increase again. It says something for the advances in medicine and our troubled perceptions that patients are reported now to be more scared of catching a hospital infection than of undergoing surgery. But even if MRSA is vanquished, that fear will never disappear entirely – not while death remains the great "undiscovered country", and mortality such a problem for us.

■ ■ ■

I have recently been admitted to Intensive Care, and I am feeling fretful, feverish and frightened. It is evening, I think, and I ask for Anna to be called to come and sit with me for comfort. This is the only time I make such a request, but the message never reaches her, and I remain alone. So I ask the nurses if they will hold my hand. Just for a few minutes to calm and settle me. They are tremendously caring. They tenderly manoeuvre me to change my sweaty sheets, or patiently prepare cold compresses for my burning forehead. But this request seems to embarrass them. "When I've finished this," or "When I've done that," they reply. I have no recollection of whether they do.

Throughout my stay in hospital, but at this time in particular, my mother's visits are difficult for me. She is in the early stages of Alzheimer's Disease or some other form of dementia, which means that although she can still function relatively normally her short-term memory is poor and she repeatedly says the same things. Being asked: "How are the boys getting on at school?" or "Does Adam get a lot of homework?" three or four times in the space of as many minutes is a minor trial of anyone's patience. For me, in my severely weakened condition, it is more than I have the strength to bear. Nevertheless, what my mother still understands with undimmed maternal instinct is the comfort of being touched when you are feeling distressed and vulnerable. My happiest moments with her during these months are spent in silence simply holding hands.

Poignantly, when she later becomes ill herself, she frustrates my father in his efforts to feed and look after her by constantly demanding that he should lie down on the bed next to her so that they can hold one another. Sadly, she doesn't seek support in this way from her children. Perhaps the sense of her role as a mother is still too strong – you cuddle and comfort your little ones, they don't comfort you.

■ ■ ■

The healing power of touch has a potent and well-attested history that goes back far further than the fear of hospitals. It has of course biblical manifestations and significance. The sick with "divers diseases" were brought to Jesus, "and he laid his hands on every one of them, and healed them." He even touched lepers, demonstrating thereby not only his compassion, but also his identification or kinship with "unclean" and sinful men. (The fact that he did not contract their disease has been interpreted – originally by St Paul – as a sign that although he was "touched by the feeling of our infirmities", he did not succumb to human weakness.)

These days we may be more inclined to view the restorative power of touch in psychological rather than directly physical terms, but it remains a potent force. Princess Diana made a palpable difference to the lives of many AIDS patients by holding hands with one of them, and having her photograph taken while she did so.

Traditionally, the heart of any doctor's consultation was a manual examination. He (for usually it was he) touched his patient as part of the process of diagnosing and then treating him. But ever since René Laennec invented the stethoscope in 1816, the contact has become increasingly removed. These days the physician is more likely to use a needle to take a blood sample or a "dipstick" to obtain a swab. If he ventures out from behind his computer to touch the patient, it will be with hands encased in sterile gloves. He may even don a plastic apron as well.

■ ■ ■

While recuperating after surgery, I receive a visit from one of the hospital chaplains. We talk for a time, and as he is leaving the priest asks whether I would like him to "lay hands" on me while he says a prayer. Although I believe in a sort of transcendant humanism which might be termed "divine", I fiercely resist any idea of God as some sort of cosmic magician. Nevertheless, I feel I have nothing to lose and so accept the offer – and find what follows a truly extraordinary experience. As the priest places his hands on my head, I feel an intense, warm glow passing between them and my scalp. I pay no attention to what he is saying because I am transfixed by the energy being transmitted through his palms. The sensation lasts no more than a few seconds, and I am not instantly cured – rather the opposite if anything since the effects of my illness still dog me to this day. However, the experience itself remains vividly memorable, and continues to seem rather wonderful.

■ ■ ■

I do not wish to suggest that hospital staff should all be laying on hands or indulging in empty rituals of sensual healing. But being touched is a way in which our humanity is affirmed, in which our connectedness is, quite literally, made manifest to us. These are vital aspects of our sense of well-being. It is surely not a matter of mere chance that alternative therapies are currently enjoying a surge in popularity, and that so many of these involve touching the patient. Reflexology, kinesiology, aromatherapy and other forms of healing massage, cranial osteopathy, even reiki, all entail physical contact with the therapist. One of very few good memories I have from my time in ITU is of being visited by Keith, the Royal Free's complementary therapies co-ordinator. For ten blissful minutes, I temporarily forgot my pain and distress while he gently massaged my feet and calves. It was a marvellously soothing and comforting sensation.

Hospitals are frequently dehumanising places where our dignity and self-worth are stripped away. The fear they provoke may never be removed entirely, but it can be heightened or reduced. Part of making them less frightening may perhaps be about deciding whether they should be institutions that affirm or deny the importance of touch.

CHAPTER
13

MRSA

"It may seem a strange principle to enunciate as the very first requirement in a Hospital that it should do no harm."

FLORENCE NIGHTINGALE

"MRSA, the hospital superbug" – the phrase has become a mantra, endlessly repeated on a daily basis in the press and other media. It is perhaps only to be expected that "superhospitals" would meet their nemesis in a ubiquitous "superbug". All that is required now is a super-hero to come and vanquish it, but although there are plenty to choose from in contemporary cinema and cartoons, the real world is a different matter and our beleaguered hospitals still wait in vain for liberation.

For certainly this is a mighty foe with which they are confronted. Not only has it "undermined public confidence in hospitals" according to a recent survey conducted by the NHS Confederation. It was also the central issue of the Conservative Party's 2005 General Election campaign. It has prompted a review of hospital visiting hours and practice, and been associated – at least by *The Times* – with the unprecedented criminal trial over the death of a patient in which the Southampton University Hospitals NHS Trust was prosecuted under the Health and Safety at Work Act for failing to run Southampton General Hospital in a way that ensured patient safety was not put at risk. In keeping with its superstar status, it has even laid claim to its first superstar victim, with the Great Train Robber and folk hero Ronnie Biggs being reported as "close to death" after contracting MRSA while having "routine treatment" in hospital following a series of strokes. Interestingly, though, several months after this report appeared Biggs was still alive, and it was *his* nemesis – Jack Slipper "of the Yard" – who had died in the meantime. For despite its awesome reputation, the reality of having MRSA – at least in my experience – is banal in the extreme. There are no obvious symptoms, and I receive no apparent treatment. There is certainly no dramatic life and death struggle with this "killer" bug as it colonizes my body.

What I do have to endure though is the inconvenience and mild discomfort of nurses taking weekly swabs from various sensitive parts of my body, such as my nose, perineum and (surgical) wound site. I also find my visitors having to perform some slightly curious rituals when they come to see me – wiping their hands with alcohol gel as they depart, and wearing wafer-thin, white plastic aprons throughout their time in my company, which are then removed and thrown away as they leave. These aprons look fine over nurses' uniforms. Even if they suggest that the wearer is about to put you through some messy procedure involving blood or other bodily fluids (such as having your body greased like Marlow in *The Singing Detective*), they still seem sensible and functional. But over a surgeon's suit, or most other forms of regular day-wear, they assume a slightly surreal appearance – as if they are part of some curious Masonic ritual not fit to be mentioned in polite company or undertaken in normal clothes.

The bug not only involves staff "dressing up". It also makes them extremely jumpy. Even after giving three clear sets of swabs, which mean I no longer have the infection, I still find myself being treated with extreme caution. On one occasion I am hurriedly shunted from a surgical ward to an isolation room in the Ophthalmic Ward three floors below after staff find MRSA mentioned in my notes. On another, a nurse administering one of my short-stay re-admissions stubbornly and quite unnecessarily insists on taking a further set of swabs before allowing me in.

But, generally, having MRSA in itself seems to make little difference to me. Indeed, on the upside, it means that when I leave Intensive Care I am housed in a separate room rather than on a shared ward – which since I have to stay there for a further three months is a far from negligible benefit.

In fact, the problems and dangers posed by MRSA bear no relation to its immense, headline-grabbing status. Over the past few years there have been some 7500 cases of MRSA in UK hospitals each year, resulting in an annual total of 1200–1400 deaths (though some press reports put this figure as high as 5000 deaths per year). Either way, these are among the highest figures in Europe. However, compared with, say, heart disease or most forms of cancer the total numbers are trifling, and even the survival rates are distinctly less than terrifying. So what is this mysterious, so-called "superbug", and why has it acquired such a fearsome reputation?

Methicillin-resistant *Staphylococcus aureus* is quite simply a bacterium or bug that is resistant to antibiotics. In itself the *Staphylococcus aureus* germ is fairly innocuous. It is actually found on the skin of about three in ten healthy people, and many of those who "develop" MRSA in hospital are in fact carrying the bug when they are admitted. The problems occur when the bacteria invade the skin and cause infection – particularly of surgical wounds. *Staphylococcus aureus* can then get into the bloodstream and cause more serious infections such as blood poisoning (septicaemia), lung infection (pneumonia), bone infection (osteomyelitis) or heart valve infection (endocarditis). These are most likely to occur in those who are already unwell or debilitated (i.e. seriously ill hospital patients), and can prove fatal.

So while my continuing infection with MRSA once I leave Intensive Care might seem fairly trifling and innocuous, the pneumonia I contract while in ITU (most probably as a result of having MRSA) most definitely is not. Having a hole drilled through my ribs or even a pipe thrust down my throat while performing breathing exercises in order to treat the pneumonia are painful experiences that I have no wish to repeat.

Nevertheless, the clamour surrounding MRSA is not down simply to the danger of the infections that it can precipitate and the unpleasantness of their treatments. It is the result of the fact that it is a disease which ought to be preventable, but which, once acquired, is difficult to cure. For these reasons it touches upon and unleashes a number of profound anxieties about hospitals that are part of the contemporary *zeitgeist*.

The first anxiety concerns cleanliness. MRSA is spread by person-to-person contact (often by passive or healthy "carriers"), and also by touching sheets, towels, dressings and so forth which have been used by someone who has MRSA. The number of cases of MRSA can therefore be kept down if hospitals practise good hygiene measures. This means staff washing their hands after contact with patients and before undertaking any procedure, proper disinfecting and disposal of equipment such as catheters and drips (flexible endoscopes, for instance, cannot be sterilised by heat), and the regular cleaning of wards and bedding. Because dust and surfaces can become contaminated with the organism, wiping and washing all surfaces is important to the prevention of MRSA. But the sad fact is that many modern hospitals – and the Royal Free is no exception to this – are dirty places.

Over the past 30 years, there has been a huge change of culture in our society whereby power structures have become less fixed and hierarchical, more fluid and provisional, as organisations seek constantly to adapt to a world that is being rapidly and endlessly transformed. Career ladders and jobs for life are things of the past. Yesterday's formality and sense of place have given way to more casual behaviour and styles of management. Hospitals – although still highly ordered institutions in comparison with many – have not been immune to this process. Indeed, the NHS has probably been re-organized more frequently than any other institution in the country – once every six years according to a recent report. At a local or operational level, this shift has been manifest in the demise of the hospital matron and the rise of the NHS Trust Chief Executive. More trivially, it is seen in the disappearance of nurses' starched white aprons and black polished shoes, and their replacement with easy-care trousers and scuffed trainers.

With this have come concerns about the loss of authority and the disintegration of order and chains of command. Cleaners are frequently no longer employed by the hospitals they work in, but by commercial companies paid to provide cleaning services. So who supervises the cleaners? Who is ensuring their work is done properly, and setting the standards by which it is assessed?

For want of anything better to do during my many months in hospital, I often watch the cleaners at work and am struck by several things. One is the unpredictable timetable by which they seem to operate. The work to be done each day remains fairly constant, and therefore one might expect some sort of regular routine. But the floor-sweeping during the morning one day, which is then completed by washing it and cleaning the bathrooms several hours later, is changed to a single visit at lunchtime the next day in which everything is done, and then perhaps followed by no visit at all the day after that.

I am also aware of the frequent churlishness or weary impatience with which the work is undertaken. Unsurprisingly perhaps given the nature of their job, the cleaners often seem slightly irritated by patients sitting where they need to sweep. The floor is laboriously mopped, but without much vigour or concern if patches are missed; and the walls are never washed, so that faded smears of blood or stains from spilt food or drinks linger for days, or even weeks, on end.

More important, however, is the fact that although I regularly encounter smelly, unventilated toilets and dank bathrooms that resemble the rancid, sodden changing rooms of a run-down municipal swimming pool, I never see anyone inspect the cleaners' work after it has been completed. Certainly, a supervisor or "line manager" from the cleaning company that services the Royal Free is an unknown species on the wards there. And the nurses have more pressing things to do and evidently do not consider it within their remit to check up on the work of the domestic staff.

It therefore comes as no surprise that when a BBC documentary entitled *A Dirty Weekend in Hospital* mischievously arranges for a number of small items such as a curtain hook and piece of loose change to be left in the wards and toilets of the Royal Free, these objects remain unmoved several days later – along with a pair of latex gloves that have been discarded, presumably by a member of staff, in one of the hospital lifts. No one bothers to clean them up – or notices that they haven't been. It does, however, make it more than a little ironic to read in a recent item of "Trust News" about MRSA on the Royal Free website that "Wards are inspected regularly to check cleanliness" and "Each ward has a lead nurse (the equivalent of the 'modern matrons' referred to by the health secretary) and many have a housekeeper." The ward on which I spend most time has an excellent, if hard-pressed, sister, but to compare her authority and brief to that of a matron – certainly an "old-fashioned one" – is fatuous. It also has a housekeeper – a genial, little

Irish woman who kindly offers to toast your bread at breakfast time. But if the hospital is expecting this timid, deferential creature, who is only one step up in its hierarchy from the cleaners and other domestic staff, to be in the forefront of stamping out MRSA and ensuring that rigorous standards of cleanliness are enforced, then it is no surprise that the "superbug" remains an issue.

In her book *Purity and Danger*, the anthropologist Mary Douglas suggests that our ideas of cleanliness and dirt are not based purely on issues of hygiene derived from the 19th century discovery of the bacterial transmission of disease, but have their roots in much older concepts of dirt, which are essentially "matter out of place". She also proposes that when authority is weak and social order under threat "we find pollution ideas come to their support".

This has an intriguing relevance to the media obsession with MRSA. For many years now, the majority of our newspapers have pursued an ideological theme of failing public institutions and the inadequacy of state-run services. MRSA seemingly offers a perfect demonstration of their shortcomings, while simultaneously suggesting a need for stronger authority, for more order and control. This was surely the reasoning behind the Conservative Party's adoption of the issue during the 2005 General Election campaign. "It can't be hard to clean a hospital ward," their advertising implied. "It must be down to bad management. Elect us, and we'll provide stronger, better management."

There was, however, a huge irony in this attempt to exploit public anxiety about declining authority and our fragmenting social order. For underlying the concern about MRSA and cleanliness in hospitals is a further anxiety – that they may be the result of "creeping privatisation" and "putting private profit ahead of public good". The Conservative-led drive over the past 25 years to cut costs and improve efficiency in the public sector by privatisation and the contracting out of services such as cleaning or maintenance has come under pressure in the wake of events such as the Hatfield and Potters Bar rail crashes. MRSA is the medical equivalent of these. Has the attempt to save money (and simultaneously build in a profit margin) simply backfired? Is it any wonder that our hospitals are dirty if their cleaners are underpaid and exploited by companies more concerned about their financial bottom line? Is there an irreconcilable conflict between public safety and the demands of running a competitive business that inevitably leads to corner-cutting and the decline of standards? Whether or not these fears are justified, they are certainly part of the mental climate in which MRSA has flourished; and my experience suggests that there is unquestionably a problem regarding chains of command, and how responsibility is apportioned, that the privatisation of services within the NHS has created.

There is also a third anxiety connected to hygiene or cleanliness that MRSA has touched, and that concerns racial shifts and the increasing multiculturalism of our society. For the fact is that almost all the hospital cleaners I have personally encountered are either Asian or black – most seem to be Afro-Caribbean women in their 40s and 50s. If there is a suspicion that they are not doing their job properly, then there cannot help but be a racial element to this.

Furthermore, it has been suggested that the spread of MRSA has been exacerbated by more relaxed hospital visiting rules – less restriction of visitor times and numbers – which are now being tightened up again. "Patients are tired and unwell, and ten family members sitting on the edge of the bed doesn't seem a good idea," the Chief Executive of the NHS is quoted as saying in one newspaper report about measures to tackle MRSA. However, it is predominantly patients of Asian and Middle Eastern origin whose families "move in" en masse and pass the whole day with their ailing relative, rather than their Caucasian counterparts, whose visitors tend to be fewer and stay for shorter times. Again, the concern with MRSA and infection control seems to be fuelled by latent anxiety about the changing complexion of our society and mistrust of its implications.

Beyond the concern about cleanliness, however, and the different anxieties that underpin it, there are two other major fears relating to hospitals that contribute to our seeming national obsession with MRSA. The first is a mistrust of science. With its amazing surgical and diagnostic machinery, its analytical laboratories and battery of life-saving drugs, the modern hospital is a monument to the extraordinary scientific progress of the past two centuries. But for all its increasingly sophisticated technology and treatments, this is not an environment in which most of us feel comfortable or at ease. Scientific progress has never been unambiguously beneficial. It has brought us nuclear weapons as well as the X-ray machine – and even the X-ray machine, in its latest refinements such as CT scanners as much as in its more primitive forms, carries dangers as well as benefits. We are doubtful about the ethical and moral implications of organ transplants, genetic testing and manipulation, or *in vitro* fertilisation. And so, as many science fiction writers have realized and exploited in their work, we are very open to the idea that the progress of science is an act of hubris or folly on the part of mankind, for which Nature may in due course exact a terrible revenge. Thalidomide, radiation-related cancer, MRSA – all can be seen in different ways as sobering examples of the dangers of science. We develop ever more powerful antibiotics to combat disease, but use them excessively or unnecessarily, and Nature is not to be so easily outwitted and defeated. It produces a germ that resists antibiotics and attacks people at the very heart of our scientifically-led attempts to eliminate and deny illness: in hospital. The symmetry or "justice" is so perfect that it could come from fiction; but MRSA is real enough, and this gives it an even greater hold on our imaginations.

The other great anxiety that MRSA touches is our fear of death. Quite simply, in a culture that is in huge collective denial about mortality, it offers an uncomfortable reminder that hospital is not somewhere we go to get better but – for 62 per cent of us anyway – somewhere that we die. My original title for this book was "The Sickness Factory", by which I wished to draw attention to the fact that hospitals manufacture illness as well as process and cure it. This has always been part of their heritage and possibly always will be. However, it is a massive affront to our sense of order and propriety if hospitals appear to be places that make people ill rather than better. We can just about accept that behind closed doors – or at least closed curtains – hospitals may occasionally lose the fight against human frailty and patients "pass away". But the idea that the hospital has actively caused their deaths is more than we can bear. That forces us to confront the grim reality of all medical institutions, and deal with their indissoluble association with suffering, pain and human decay – to acknowledge their uncomfortable and unmentionable role as a stepping stone to the grave. Such a painful reminder constitutes a scandal that must be blazoned across the tabloids and eradicated immediately.

When the sparkling new University College London Hospital opened its doors to the public in the summer of 2005, the accompanying fanfares of publicity emphasized not its state-of-the-art facilities and equipment, but the number of wash hand-basins and single rooms "to help in our fight against MRSA". The Trust Chairman proudly proclaimed that "infection control teams have had a hand in almost every aspect of the hospital – from the fabric used in furnishings to the surfaces used on the floors". Here was a building not made of grimy bricks or crumbling, dirty concrete, but of glistening steel and glass that attested to its unimpeachable cleanliness. What the press releases did not mention, however, was that ever-increasing patient turnover – which is also part of this brave new world and a pre-requisite of the hospital meeting its performance targets and balancing its books – inevitably militates against better infection control.

Since the profoundly disturbing events of 9/11, the first decade of the 21st century has been frequently – but usefully – characterized as an "age of anxiety". Living in such a time, it is perhaps inevitable that we should be pre-occupied with "superbugs" and the capacity of hospitals to cause harm, rather than celebrating the good they do and the miraculous cures they effect. It is a curious, and in many way distorted, perspective, rooted in an unrealistic wish to deny medicine its "dark side" and ignore the dangers that inevitably accompany medical treatment. However, although the importance of MRSA has been exaggerated because of the deeper fears and anxieties it provokes, its significance – as a largely preventable calamity – is no less profound if you happen to be a victim. Had I died of pneumonia in Intensive Care, my attitude – or that of my relatives – to the furore that surrounds the infection would doubtless be very different.

CHAPTER
14

PRISON

"He walked out through the hospital gates thinking to himself:
It's just like leaving prison."

ALEKSANDR SOLZHENITSYN Cancer Ward

If my room at the Royal Free overlooking Hampstead and the Heath
were a private flat, the view would be worth a small fortune. I enjoy it
through the changing seasons as the dull brown outlines of the trees
gradually turn to gloriously burgeoning green. And yet, for all its
beauty, my time spent here is one of – if not *the* – most miserable periods of my life. How I yearn to escape!

In the vain hope that not eating might allow my fistula to heal itself,
the doctors steadfastly continue drip-feeding me for week after week. I
wait in desperation for permission even to start drinking juices or
soups again as this will mark the first step towards my release, and I
find my eyes pricking with scarcely-suppressed tears each time I am
told: "Let's give it a few more days."

As I lie in my bed one evening, I think I can smell burning. I mention this to the nurse on duty, who tells me I am right – there has been a fire in one of the wards a couple of storeys below, and they have had to close it down and evacuate the patients. Meanwhile, we have just carried on as normal, seemingly oblivious.

It is early 2003. The USA and Britain are about to invade Iraq, and the world is momentarily terrified by the outbreak of SARS in Asia. The first British victim of the disease is admitted to the Royal Free for treatment. Confined in isolation, I learn about his presence in the same hospital as me from the newspapers.

■ ■ ■

A friend brings in a portable TV and VCR combi, which enables me to follow Manchester United's faltering progress in the Champions' League, and view a host of movies on tape. At home two years later, I shall come across the cassette of Steven Spielberg's *Catch Me If You Can*, which is one of the films I watch. Holding the tape again, I will find myself overwhelmed by haunting memories of loneliness and desolation.

I never want for visitors during my time in hospital, and for five months Anna religiously comes to see me every day. But despite the visitors and the kindness of the nursing staff, I finally feel unutterably alone. Shut up in hospital for a long period, you are forced to confront your own destiny, to acknowledge a painful and defining separation in the face of suffering and death. It is a sorrowful, stark experience – like that of a solitary bee, mentally confined in your own cell, amid the ceaseless activity of the hive.

■ ■ ■

I have been in two prisons in my life. One was a women's prison near Bristol, where Rose West had been detained while awaiting trial. I was filming a scene for a P D James adaptation, in which the heroine goes to visit a woman who is also being held on remand. The other was Pentonville Prison in north London, where we shot a surreal and wonderful wedding scene for a BBC2 drama in the disused "Nonce's Wing": a multi-tiered gallery of small individual cells, overlooking a central well in an isolated block shut off from the rest of the prison.

At one level, it is absurd to compare a hospital to a prison. I remember on my first visit to Pentonville being admitted to the central hub of the building, from which the different wings radiate outwards like the spokes of a wheel. There we were confronted by the prisoners, caged behind the heavy metal bars that sealed off each part of the prison. They simply stood and stared at us, alien and unwelcome intruders in their private space. Nothing could be further removed from the relentless movement of a hospital than their threatening stillness.

And yet...

■ ■ ■

When I was growing up in the mid-1960s, my grandmother developed what was then referred to as "senile dementia". She lost her short-term memory, became cantankerous and rather rude, and often reeked of urine. I remember saying to my mother that if we were going to see Nanny at Christmas, would it be possible for her to have a bath beforehand? Eventually, my grandfather no longer felt able to cope with looking after her, and she was taken away to Springfield Mental Hospital on the other side of London. I never saw her again.

My mother – an only child – bitterly regretted my Nanny's removal, and found her visits to the hospital immensely distressing. She had no wish to inflict the experience on her own young children. As a result, I have only an imaginary picture of my grandmother shut up in her ward with a group of other women whom my mother felt were in a far worse mental state than she and hastened her deterioration. However, it is not unlike that scene in Pentonville: an image of Bedlam or hell, filled with aggressive, staring faces; a tableau of lost and incarcerated souls, angry and silently accusing.

A few months after being confined, my grandmother developed pneumonia and died. It was a sad end. These days we talk about Alzheimer's Disease, of care homes rather than asylums, and of the mentally ill being "sectioned". But if you are the patient and want to leave but can't, what this means is imprisoned.

■ ■ ■

The harsh overhead lighting in Pentonville is remarkably like that found in modern hospital buildings, while the uneasy quietness I encountered there has similarities with the simmering hush sometimes heard in hospital wards at the start of visiting hours. But what really links the two is the desperate feeling of desolation, the sense of enforced isolation amid a crowd of fellow inmates. As I discovered (and shall discuss) later, the connections between hospitals and prisons are historically deep rooted and multifarious.

▪ ▪ ▪

Shut up in my room at the Royal Free, I certainly feel as if I have been incarcerated against my will – a prisoner in a brutal concrete tower, waiting for the Scarlet Pimpernel to come and rescue me… Sadly he never arrives, and I have to escape from this looming castle on my own.

Throughout my long stay in hospital, I repeatedly imagine my journey home. This begins with me striding triumphantly through the ward, saying grateful farewells to the nurses and other staff as I depart. In the event, I leave the building in a wheelchair which has faulty steering and is therefore being dragged backwards; and since there seems a good chance that I may be back the following day, I scarcely say "goodbye" to anyone as I quit the ward. But the sense of liberation I feel on passing through its doors proves no less sweet for all that.

CHAPTER
15

SHADOWS

"Life's but a walking shadow, a poor player
Who struts and frets his hour upon the stage
And then is heard no more."
WILLIAM SHAKESPEARE Macbeth

In her magnificent essay *Illness as Metaphor*, Susan Sontag eloquently describes illness as "the night-side of life, a more onerous citizenship". Robert McCrum, *The Observer*'s literary editor, has written movingly of an unseen "world of pain". For my own small part, I have come increasingly to think about the "shadow world" of the long-term sick. Whatever words you use, they describe the same thing: a realm that exists alongside the everyday world, the world of the well; one that physically inhabits the same space. But a realm that is uncomfortably dark, where everything is flat and featureless, drained of colour. It is eerily silent, but listen carefully and you will hear the cries of untold anguish with which it is filled.

Shakespeare frequently equates shadows with actors on the stage. Both are not the "real thing". And so it is when you are ill. You still see and do many of the same things. You visit the same places, encounter the same people, and still engage in conversation with them. But it is not the real thing. For you have lost the power to act. Things happen to you and around you, but you seem to have no control over them. It is a kind of half-life. You are a passive performer – playing a role, strutting and fretting, in a drama that someone else has scripted. This world of shadows, of poor players, Shakespeare also likens to a dream:

> "If we shadows have offended,
> Think but this, and all is mended:
> That you have but slumbered here
> While these visions did appear.
> And this weak and idle theme
> No more yielding but a dream"

But dreams vanish when the dreamer wakes. Shadows disappear when the light goes out. A shadow is half way to becoming a ghost, and ghosts are night-time creatures which fade "on the crowing of the cock".

■ ■ ■

The psychoanalyst Carl Gustav Jung identified the "shadow self" that appears in our dreams, the "dark side" that is now part of our vocabulary of evil thanks to fictions such as *Star Wars* and *Harry Potter*. The shadow, Jung suggests, contains the repressed and unfavourable aspects of our personality, and is engaged in conflict with the ego in a battle for deliverance. It is the regressive longing of the unconscious mind that the ego must overcome to achieve maturity, and this is symbolized as the monster or devil that the hero must fight and slay. It is Darth Vader for Luke Skywalker, Voldemort for Harry Potter. The shadow is the hero's malevolent twin, the flip-side of the heroic coin, the necessary corollary of the hero's very existence against which he defines himself.

■ ■ ■

As a hospital patient, you struggle daily to retain a foothold in the real world and live a life that has some substance. With your ability to act in any meaningful way diminished or non-existent, you are desperate to reclaim your status as a person with rounded features and a proper identity rather than be a mere dream or faceless shadow. You yearn to be more than your illness, to have a life other than just as a ghostly embodiment of the unfavourable and suppressed aspects of human existence, an unwelcome reminder of mortality which must be hidden in the shadow world of the hospital precinct.

Yet so many things in the hospital environment – the waiting (what else have you to do with your time?), the condescension ("how are *we* today?"), the assumption of incapacity ("Don't walk to X-ray, there's a wheelchair coming") – conspire to make you just that. When I am at home my GP issues prescriptions for drugs that I then take myself as directed. But if I go into hospital the nurses insist on taking those drugs from me, locking them in a cabinet beside my bed, and then giving them to me one dose at a time.

That is how life is in the shadows, in the world of the sick and suffering where treatments do not always work and where recovery – like everything else – is often agonizingly slow. So welcome to life as a spectator of your own destiny, to watching anxiously for any signs that the guttering light which gives your being any presence at all may be about to splutter and blow out.

■ ■ ■

Perhaps the problem starts with our concept of doctors. For if doctors (or indeed nurses) are to be heroes, then shadows may be their necessary counterparts, the inevitable consequence of their elevation to heroic status. In this drama patients are not people but illnesses to be combated – the demons that need to be slain, the destructive forces which must be overcome.

CHAPTER
16

THE OTHER SIDE
OF THE BED

"The web of our life is of a mingled yarn, good and ill
together;"
WILLIAM SHAKESPEARE All's Well That Ends Well

Like most people, the bulk of my experience of hospitals has been from
the patient's or visitor's side of the bed. However, I did have a brief
glimpse of how the world looks from a staff point of view (which seems
so deceptively familiar because of television hospital drama) when I
was sent by an employment agency to work as a temporary records
clerk at St Mary's Hospital, Harrow Road in 1978.

The hospital was previously known as Paddington General, but in
an attempt to shake off its poor reputation it had recently been
brought under the control of St Mary's Hospital in Paddington, which
was then riding high (Prince William was born there four years later in
the private Lindo Wing). The attempt to resuscitate the Harrow Road
Hospital clearly failed to work, however. The buildings were demol-
ished not long after to make way for a large development of luxury
flats.

I was initially assigned to the X-ray department, where my job consisted of locating any previous X-rays that the hospital held for the patients coming in to be photographed. It was pretty dull and routine work, but my days were enlivened by being privy to the "girl's locker room" chat of the radiographers.

These were all female, mostly in their 20s, and exclusively white – though with a notable Commonwealth presence from Australia and New Zealand. Although their physical environment was shabby, there was something rather pure and wholesome about these young women in their simple white dresses with cinched blue waistbands. They were all ostensibly nice, middle-class girls, but it is perhaps significant that one of my few abiding memories of them concerns a softly-rounded South African radiographer named Penny. Despite sharing the prevailing aura of innocence, I recollect her complaining airily about what a waste of time male pin-ups were. "I mean, who's interested when they've only got their penises at half-mast?" she declared in her coolly clipped accent.

I also remember a gorgeous, tall, blonde girl called Kate, who complained about her boyfriend's smelly feet and really wanted to be an air hostess with British Airways. She wasn't the brightest woman there, but I could not for the life of me understand why BA had turned her down given her looks and the fact that being a radiographer is presumably at least as intellectually demanding as being an air hostess. I also failed to understand why such an attractive creature should put up with a partner for whom, by her own admission, she spent her life buying "Odor-Eaters".

The department was overseen by one ageing, but rather distinguished-looking, (male) radiologist; and its only black face was that of a diminutive Indian woman in her 40s, who was the permanent records clerk and whom I worked alongside. Compared to the Royal Free's X-ray department today, it all seems rather touchingly old-fashioned and straightforward. No CT or MRI scanners; no Special Investigation suites; no ticket system in order just to join the queue for making an appointment. None of the multicultural presence that permeates the NHS today (though interestingly the Royal Free's radiographers still tend to be white and female with a strong antipodean representation). None of the feeling of chaotic squalor either, albeit that the fabric of the buildings was actually older and more run down. Sadly that impression seems to come from the people as much as anything, with patients untidily littering the corridors as they wait for their X-rays, and the staff rather grungily and grubbily dressed compared with their pristine predecessors.

Rather more interesting from my personal point of view was when, after a couple of weeks, I was moved on from the X-ray department to the Out-patients section of the Psychiatric Unit. This was housed in a separate building in the hospital grounds with direct access from the street so that the patients did not have to go through the main hospital complex to reach it. In-patients were housed well out of sight on the first and second floors (I never went up there), and Out-patients came in for daily clinics on the ground floor.

Again my job was to pull out the relevant background material – in this case the doctors' notes – of the incoming patients. Apart from the occasional rogue set of records, which might take the entire day to find and would involve trailing fruitlessly around the entire hospital, the work of assembling the paperwork for the following day's appointment lists was usually completed within a couple of hours. This left an awful lot of free time for reading the newspaper or, rather more grippingly, the patients' notes.

It still amazes me that whatever constraints are put on doctors and other permanent staff, I was never asked to sign any form of Official Secrets Act or Hippocratic Oath for Record Clerks in order to safeguard patient confidentiality. The implications of my looking through the patients' records were not even raised, but ensuring that the notes were complete positively required me to open the folders and check the contents.

So it was that I found myself trailing through devastating accounts of terrible mental anguish for which the only salve seemed to be the widespread distribution of palliative drugs. I soon concluded that on the scales of human suffering religion has an awful lot to answer for, with Catholicism in particular adding hugely to mankind's distress.

I was especially fascinated by the caseload of one particular doctor who specialized in dealing with people who had attempted suicide. Since the hospital serviced the wealthier properties of Maida Vale as well as less salubrious swathes of Harlesden, his patients included some well-known figures – actors and actresses, and a leading fashion and lingerie designer who had taken an overdose of pills while her husband looked on. This, it turned out, was to "punish" him for forcing her to participate in group sex sessions against her wishes. The depressing story seemed like some awful modern morality play as it sprang from the sketchy outlines of the doctor's notes – a tragic fable of someone living a lie about "the joy of sex" and paying the most dreadful price for it as they were nearly destroyed by the very thing on which their wealth and success were based. It would have been dynamite if the Sunday papers had ever got hold of it, though I doubt whether one of their accounts of its lurid details would ever have captured the rather grubby sadness that lay at its core.

Quietly shocking too, though on a much less exalted level, were the antics of Sarah, the permanent records clerk on the unit, whom I was assisting. She was a tall girl with long dark hair, in her early to mid-20s, who was obsessed by her weight and appearance. Although inclining to the fleshy, she was certainly not fat or seriously overweight. Nevertheless, spurred on by the panoply of women's magazines that she spent much of her time reading, she was consumed by the desire to shed some pounds. Despairing of achieving this by dieting, she had become convinced that slimming pills were the answer. The problem was that these were only available on prescription, and her GP would never entertain the idea of giving them to her. So, after much agonizing and debate, she eventually plucked up courage to ask one of the doctors on the unit to issue some for her.

She chose one of the registrars for her request – who was definitely the wrong man! Bespectacled, besuited and very serious, he not only turned her down flat, he also proceeded to give her a long lecture about how slimming pills were a dangerous drug, not some convenient shortcut to service her vanity. He might have saved his breath, for Sarah was an obsessive and not easily deterred. Although a bit upset by the homily, the following day she simply repeated her request to the young Irish houseman – who wrote a prescription for her on the spot. Regrettably, my stay on the unit finished at the end of the week, so I never discovered whether the pills worked.

CHAPTER
17

STAFF

"The Hospitals of London are, in many respects, noble
Institutions; in others, very defective. I think it not the least
among the instances of their mismanagement, that Ms Betsey
Prig is a fair specimen of a Hospital Nurse;"

CHARLES DICKENS Martin Chuzzlewit,
Preface to the Cheap Edition (1850)

As the titles of Peter Nichols' stage play *The National Health* and G F
Newman's television serial *The Nation's Health* suggest, the condition
of hospitals and the health service has often been viewed as a reflection
of the state of the nation. If the metaphor is a useful one, and hospitals
do offer a microcosmic image of society at large, then my recent experience of the Royal Free suggests that the age of multiculturalism and
a globalized labour force has most emphatically arrived. Without its
extraordinary, eclectic mix of staff from different parts of the world,
the hospital would simply implode. It functions as a multiracial institution or not at all.

The nurses who have looked after me include innumerable women
of black African and Afro-Caribbean origin, many Irish girls in their

20s and 30s, a wide selection of carers from the Philippines and the Far East, and even the occasional one from Egypt, Mauritius, Finland, Poland and the Czech Republic. However, during all my time in hospital, I do not think I have been attended by more than a handful of "white British" women. The small number of UK born and bred Caucasians among the nursing staff tend to be male and often gay. For some reason, there seems to be a high proportion of Australian nurses – both male and female – in ITU (while the X-ray department depends on a plethora of radiographers from New Zealand).

This international quality is not confined to London. In a recent television programme, the film director Ken Russell discussed his time in Southampton General Hospital (where he caught MRSA), and commented on the paucity of nurses there whose first language was English. This perhaps reflects not just the United Kingdom's current "open door" policy on foreign labour, but also the relatively shallow roots of nursing as a profession here. For while nursing in Catholic countries is historically linked to the charitable work of religious orders, in Protestant Britain its traditions are less long-established and austere. Only with the innovations of Elizabeth Fry and Florence Nightingale in the mid-19th century did nursing acquire a vocational flavour. Until then it was more associated with the working-class disreputableness of characters like Sarah Gamp and Betsey Prig in Charles Dickens' *Martin Chuzzlewit* (and it is perhaps not irrelevant that Dickens' charitable work extended to being an active supporter of the Royal Free.)

With the changing role of women over the past 30 years, and the erosion of the ideal of public service that has taken place during the same period, nursing in this country appears to have undergone a further mutation. The idealized "angel" of popular tradition, who selflessly devotes her life to the care of others, is no longer to be found on the wards. For most of those staffing them now, one suspects that nursing is no longer a stern social duty or quasi-religious calling. While it still requires qualities of dedication and compassion, it has become more and more like other careers, chosen from a greatly expanded range of options for the particular combination of emotional challenge, job satisfaction and financial recompense that it offers; a way of earning a living that is better rewarded in America, Australia or much of the Middle East, but, equally, is better paid in Britain than where many of the nurses working in this country were born and grew up.

The change is vividly marked in the passage from the 1970s' nurses' drama *Angels* to the recent Channel 4 series *No Angels*. "Nothing special" might be an alternative wording for the updated title, and that is certainly the premise that underlies the drama's portrayal of the nursing profession. The group of flatmates on which it centres happen to work in a hospital, but they are just like any other collection of 20-something females: more concerned with boyfriends and relationships than the substance of their jobs, constantly jockeying for power and position the same as people do in any workplace. The medical setting is incidental to their lives rather than defining.

Working conditions for nurses in London are far from attractive: apart from having to contend with the capital's property prices and its sclerotic transport system, ward staff are scheduled in exhausting 12-hour shifts with regular night duties. And if the buildings are often unsympathetic environments for patients, they are no more congenial for those who work there. Concern has been expressed recently that hospital nurses take more time off sick (an average of nearly 17 days a year) than other public sector workers – who in turn take off significantly more time than private sector employees. This may be the result of greater exposure to infection, but it also seems to reflect the increasing pressure under which nurses are working, with inflated expectations from patients and their families, poor management, and cash-strapped NHS trusts trying to save money by leaving vacancies unfilled all contributing to the problem.

There is also evidence to suggest that nursing has become less attractive and fulfilling as a result of the enlarged administrative burden that staff now face, with up to 40 per cent of their time taken up with form-filling and other non-clinical work. I myself have been repeatedly baffled and irritated on my frequent return visits to hospital for one or two night stays by having to spend half an hour or more with a nurse while she takes down my extensive "patient history". Since the past never changes, the vast bulk of it is always the same as on the previous occasion, and its many convolutions have already been thoroughly documented in my ever-expanding notes, which are now the thickness of several telephone directories.

Despite the problems, however, what is remarkable about the Royal Free is the relative stability of the nursing staff. Many of the faces on the wards remain the same as when I first visited Anna there more than six years ago. Those who have left generally seem to have done so for reasons of career advancement, to return abroad, or to have children, not because they were disaffected and could no longer take the stress. From the patient's point of view, this continuity is immensely desirable. Not just because of the warmth with which you are greeted if you are unfortunate enough to have to be re-admitted, but because a nurse who knows the ward well is more efficient and provides better care.

I used to dread the nights when agency staff were allocated to look after me. Not knowing where things were stored, they would be much slower in responding to requests for banal but vital things such as urine bottles. Not knowing me or much of my history, they would also tend to be inflexible and suspicious, doggedly insisting that I should be given drugs that I hadn't taken for days because "you're still written up for them on your chart", or getting panicky and rushing to send for a doctor when my temperature was slightly raised although it was doing no more than follow a well-established pattern.

Although the hospital's blue-uniformed nurses can sometimes seem a little mechanical in the way they go about their tasks, they are nevertheless unsurprisingly zealous when set alongside the green-clad domestic staff. These are mostly middle-aged women of colour who give the impression of being wearied by life and go about their work with matter-of-fact economy of effort. Cleaning other people's mess is hardly a job to set the pulse racing, and the cleaners in particular often seem bored and verging on disaffection. Patients and visitors who obstruct their work are clearly an irritant, and the job is doubtless unfulfilling and poorly paid. Predictably therefore, the standard to which it is so laboriously completed is seldom more than adequate.

At the other end of the hospital hierarchy are the doctors, with the consultants representing the visible power in the system. Their ward rounds are a reminder of how structured and deferential the medical profession remains, with teams of registrars and housemen nervously responding to cross-examination about the patients' progress, and the ward sister or lead nurse earnestly transcribing the care commands from the white-coated gods on high. At the Royal Free, there are more white faces among the doctors than among the other staff, with the consultants in particular continuing to be predominantly white British men with a slightly patrician air. But the ranks of junior surgeons and other physicians now conform to the general pattern of the hospital and have a strongly international flavour. I have been treated by Russian, Italian, Indian, Greek, Egyptian and Pakistani doctors, a fair proportion of whom have been women, as well as operated upon by a consultant surgeon of African descent.

The consultants may appear to be "top of the ant heap", with all the other categories of staff scurrying around below, but in fact their power is circumscribed – "cog-like not God-like" as frustrated senior doctor Raymond Tallis has described them when writing about the NHS. While consultants have absolute hegemony over matters under their direct control like operating lists, they are subject as much as anyone to the constraints of the system and there is much that eludes their grasp. The imperious commands of one day's ward round are often met with a litany of excuses and failed responses the next. The junior doctors grimly confess that they are still waiting for X-ray to come up with a time for the ultrasound, haven't received the results of the blood test, or remain unable to find the missing notes. I have sometimes noticed an air of weary bemusement in my consultants as they apologise for X-rays having disappeared, or express surprise at clinic appointments having been postponed without their being informed and through no desire or fault of their own. Despite the deference of the nursing staff and junior doctors, their carefully cultivated surface of authority often seems wafer-thin as they struggle to make the hospital machinery work.

That machinery is a vast and complex structure. It embraces a posse of polo-shirted physiotherapists – predominantly white Britons who seem to spend much of their time flirting with the nurses, if male; or cultivating a strict no-nonsense manner (which might alternatively be described as bullying), if female. It includes multiple phlebotomists, who circulate the wards taking blood samples with wondrous, painless efficiency, and for some reason seem mostly to come from Eastern Europe. There are pharmacists and dieticians – usually women and frequently of Asian origin – whose tasks are to organize patients' medication or advise on nutrition and recommend food supplements. Ferrying beds and wheelchairs to and from the operating theatres or the X-ray department are the hospital porters – all men, mostly in their 20s and 30s, and from a wide variety of ethnic backgrounds, but with the unifying characteristic of all seeming to be slightly anarchic "chancers". On a recent stay, I was particularly enchanted by one who was unable to speak, but communicated through an extraordinary combination of whistles, hand gestures and vividly expressive eyes.

The happiest staff often appear to be those on the fringes of the system or occupying very specific niches within it: Keith, the complementary therapies co-ordinator, and his team of volunteers who clearly enjoy giving massages to patients; the stoma nurses; or those overseeing chemotherapy treatments. These reveal the human face of the system, often working well beyond their allotted hours and making space to accommodate patients' needs with an attitude of "We'll slot you in somewhere."

Less at ease are the clinic clerks and receptionists, many of whom seem harassed and anxious, presumably from constant exposure to fretful and frustrated patients. Although doing no more than "obeying orders" that emanate from elsewhere, they represent the machine at work, unable and sometimes also unwilling to respond to the anxiety and individual circumstances of those with whom they are dealing.

With no seeming awareness of contradiction or inconsistency, the hospital also employs a team of counsellors – in the case of the one I saw, a sympathetic Jewish woman with immense dark eyes and a strong hint of mittel-Europe in her accent and manner. There are also Catholic and Anglican chaplains who stalk the building with portable Eucharist kits in their bags. One of these is a young-ish female priest who, it transpires, has become a minor television personality.

It is an immense plethora of staff that inhabits the building – a bewildering network of different skills and human types which gives the impression that all of life is to be found there; a country in its own right, even before the patients are admitted, which readily explains why hospitals are often seen as metaphors for the society from which they emanate. So how does this "Little Britain" function? Does it work?

In terms of its multicultural composition, which is perhaps its most defining characteristic, the answer is emphatically yes. People of all colours and backgrounds rub along and work together in a way that seems largely free of racial tension or prejudice. That may be found among some of the patients, and there may be legitimate criticisms across the health service as a whole concerning equality in the pace of career advancement, but on a day-to-day basis, the Royal Free seems a remarkably harmonious environment, particularly given the stressful nature of the work that goes on there.

Whether, or how well, the hospital functions as a caring institution – whether it represents a benign, humane and well-ordered society – is a more difficult question to answer. The institution is reasonably well resourced, but looking at the issue in terms of staff, it has to be said that the overall impression is less one of tightly-knit organization, than of tolerably functioning muddle. The individuals who work there inevitably comprise the good, the bad and the ugly. The booking clerk who sought to dissuade a friend of mine from cancelling an appointment by officiously and irrelevantly informing him that "This procedure costs £1000, you know" goes about his tasks alongside Mr Thomas who "popped in" every day over the Easter holiday weekend when I was there to ensure that his patients were all right. Collectively, however, one has the feeling that the commitment and professionalism of the staff are often compromised by working in an environment that controls them rather than vice versa. It seems to frustrate them with its inadequacies rather than excite them with its possibilities. The result is a hospital in which the employees are generally positive and motivated, but of which they are perhaps less than wholly proud; a place where the struggle of getting the job done often seems to eclipse the reason for doing it. Not a callous institution, but a pushed and therefore inward-looking and sometimes careless one.

Is that a reflection of the country at large? A fair image of Britain under new Labour in the early years of the 21st century? It seems curiously appropriate that the abortive terrorist attacks in Glasgow and London during the early summer of 2007 were organized by staff working in the NHS. For with its chaotic mix of cost imperatives, elusive sources of responsibility, bureaucratic structures and social concern, the modern superhospital certainly embodies the messy and sometimes contradictory goals of a multiracial society working to maintain its position and preserve its humanity in a divided, shifting and increasingly competitive world.

CHAPTER
18

DEATH

"How quiet death is."

JOHN KEATS Endymion

In common with most hospitals, Death haunts the precincts of the Royal Free like a silent, but ever-present, shadow. Yet the prevailing impression of the place is not one of morbidity, but of teeming, albeit sometimes spectral, life. Direct encounters with Death, at least in most wards, are comparatively rare. I become aware of only one fatality on the ward where I spend the vast bulk of my time during the whole of my five-month stay. One morning Karen, the ebullient Irish nurse, seems in an unusually subdued mood, and soon tells me quietly: "We had a death on the ward last night. An old gentleman passed away…" However, things prove dramatically different when I return for repair surgery on my leaking wound some 15 months later.

The day I check in, I am joined by a tall, rather gaunt man in his mid-40s called Peter, who occupies the bed opposite mine. He has a slightly manic, distracted air, and eagerly devours the evening paper. He then proceeds to ring a number of his friends and berate them about David James – the first-choice England goalkeeper at this time –

who, he insists, has less ability than any number of players to be seen on Hackney Marshes on a Sunday morning. In age, appearance, and with his rather febrile intelligence, Peter reminds me a little of the actor Richard E Grant. Perhaps this time the Scarlet Pimpernel really is going to keep an eye on me and ensure my early release...

Following my operation the next day, I am moved, as is customary, to the bay of four beds for high dependency patients, which is opposite the nurses' desk in the centre of the ward. A day or two later, presumably after his own operation, Peter joins me there. He seems much the same in his uncompromising assertiveness, but post-operative pain and immobility do not bring out the best in anyone. Together with the two other acute patients in the bay, we all pursue our own strategies for gaining the nurses' attention and assistance, and grow tetchy and frustrated when we fail to receive the help we require.

One evening Peter is visited by his father, and an argument flares up between them. The substance seems to be that one of the nursing staff has told Peter that he is being difficult about something (which may well be true – he is not an easy personality). His father, who is a sympathetic and still youthful man in his 60s, has overheard the remark, and made a throwaway riposte that this is scarcely unusual. Peter is quietly furious with him, and vents his annoyance with hissing spleen. There is still a mood of simmering resentment when his father leaves shortly after. An hour or two later, Peter telephones home, and continues to tell him how betrayed he feels. "I need your support, not be undermined by you," he fumes. "You're my family, remember?" But the conversation clearly achieves little, and Peter still seems piqued when he hangs up.

The next morning Peter is shaving with the curtains drawn around his bed when his consultant pays his morning visit. The surgeon peers through a gap in the curtains, and jovially tells Peter what a wonderful sight he looks shaving with a gastric tube coming out of his nostril. Happy to see his patient out of bed, the doctor says he won't interrupt and continues on his way.

Not long after, there is a loud crash from behind the curtains. One of the nurses goes to investigate, and evidently discovers that Peter has fallen over. I hear her pick him up and then sit him in a chair beside his bed. All seems to go quiet, and I return my attention to the book I am reading.

Then suddenly the sound of Peter's staccato, panic-filled voice cuts through the air.

"I … can't… breathe," he gasps – and immediately all hell breaks loose.

The nurse hits the "crash button", and the alarm echoes violently through the ward. Staff come racing into the bay from all sides. They want to gain access to Peter, so fling open the curtains around his bed and swiftly draw the ones round the other three. "Call the Crash Team," someone shouts. Amid the chaos as my curtains close I catch a glimpse of Janet, the ward sister, as she takes a deep breath and seems momentarily to be calling up her years of training before she launches into leading the attempts to resuscitate the stricken man.

Before long the Crash Team arrive to take control, and the sounds of frantic, rather confused, improvisation rapidly turn into a familiar and well-rehearsed scene from *Casualty* or *ER*.

"First adrenalin shot going in now," I hear through the curtains. The team obviously carry some form of mobile computer to regulate their drills, as a mechanical American voice then cuts in counting down the seconds from 30.

"Stand back," says a real voice at the bedside, and I imagine Peter's body jolting violently as the pads are applied to kick-start his heart.

The situation now seems to be well under control.

"Second adrenalin shot going in," says one of the team calmly. They begin to talk quietly among themselves. I can't hear what is being said, but it seems to be social chit-chat, not urgent medical team-speak. The quiet hum of conversation continues, and I pick up my book again. Not surprisingly, though, I find it hard to concentrate on reading it.

Perhaps 15 or 20 minutes later, Janet, the ward sister, slips through the curtains to see me.

"Are you all right?" she enquires.

"Yes, I'm fine," I reply, perhaps not entirely truthfully – but all things are relative. "How's Peter?" A momentary look of panic flickers in Janet's eyes.

"I'm afraid…" she begins. There is a hint of tears before she takes another breath and continues:

"I'm afraid he died."

I am stunned. There has been nothing to suggest this. No slightly desperate voice saying "I think we're losing him." No sober pronouncements declaring it is too late and that he's gone. Not even a rhetorical question from the team leader, " I think we should stop, if you all agree?" followed by the stony statement: "Rescuss abandoned 10.23. Thank you very much everyone." This isn't like a scene from *Casualty* at all. A young-ish man has died some five or six metres from where I am sitting, and I had no idea. I think of his poor father and the row they never made up.

"But – what did he die of?" I ask, baffled and confused. Janet again looks slightly uncomfortable.

"I'm afraid I'm not allowed to discuss it," she answers, with a hint of apology in her voice. There is a pause, then she adds: "But he was really very unwell," as if that somehow makes it better. I think for her, since they have failed to save his life, it probably does.

Eventually, the curtains around my bed are opened. There is a gap in the space diagonally opposite where Peter's bed had been, and a heavy silence hangs over the entire ward. A nurse comes and quietly wheels away Peter's beside table with his belongings in it. Later a cleaner arrives with a machine to polish the empty floor. It is as if they are trying to clean away all traces of Peter and erase the shock of his death. But the gloomy mood persists, and only the hum of the polishing machine interrupts the quietness.

Nevertheless, by tea-time a new patient has arrived to fill the void, restoring the bay to full capacity. Janet enquires whether I would like to move beds, as my condition no longer requires constant surveillance. I say I don't want to be any trouble, and decline.

Peter died on Friday morning. There is some shuffling of beds over the weekend, which brings an elderly but still sprightly man named David into the position immediately opposite mine. He is courteous and friendly, and has a sympathetic-looking wife who is probably ten years his junior. However, my abiding memory of him comes from when he tries going for walk round the ward on Sunday evening. He forgets that he has a catheter attached to his penis which leads via a flexible rubber tube to a urine bottle hanging on his bed. After he has taken six or seven strides, the rubber tube refuses to stretch any further and snaps back violently with an almighty "twang". I gasp at the sound and wince at the thought of the immense tug it must have given on his male member, presumably stretching it like the straining tube. Fortunately, David seems comparatively undeterred.

However, early on Monday morning his condition starts to give cause for concern. I am unsure what the exact problem is – something to do with excess fluid, I think I hear – but the curtains are drawn round his bed and the doctor called. His consultant, Mr Thomas, comes to see him along with the rest of his team, and they all look anxious. Even after their departure, the mood of sombre watchfulness continues.

After breakfast, one of the junior sisters slips through the curtains to check on his condition, and her raised voice is to be heard immediately calling "David…David," as she tries to rouse him. He has evidently passed out. Within a few seconds the noise of the crash alarm once more echoes round the ward, and a now-familiar routine begins again. Staff come racing. The curtains are drawn round my own bed. The Crash Team arrive. But it is all quieter and less dramatic this time. No computerized countdowns, or matter-of-fact announcements about injections being given. I can hear very little and have no real idea what is going on.

Some time later, Janet comes in to see me once again. She seems calmer, less shaken on this occasion.

"Is David all right?" I ask. I am not sure what answer I expect, but am still slightly taken aback when she shakes her head and says:

"We weren't able to save him, I'm afraid. He died."

Once again, someone's life has come to an end within a few feet of where I am sitting, and I haven't realized. Death seems to be moving in a clockwise direction around the bay, and next bed in line is my own. I do not fancy waiting to see whether he strikes in threes and a further visitation is shortly to be paid.

"Do you think I could move beds later?" I ask. "I'm not sure I like it here anymore."

"Of course," Janet replies. Then she adds: "It's not always like this, you know."

I am not sure either of us could cope if it were.

As Janet leaves, I catch sight through my curtains of David's wife (now his widow) arriving, red-eyed and clearly struggling to control her emotions. She pauses and tries to collect herself for a moment before slipping in to see his corpse.

Towards lunchtime, I am taken with my bed and belongings to a room down the ward corridor towards the exit. It seems to be progress in the right direction. Even there though, the mood is once more sober and subdued, the nurses evidently upset by another death so close at hand, even if the patients here are not even aware of what has taken place.

During the afternoon, I notice that the doors to the room are quietly closed for a few minutes without any explanation being offered. I may be wrong, but I sense that David's body has been kept in one of the treatment rooms and is now being taken away. Although his presence still hangs heavily on the ward, Death is now being silently removed, hidden from sight and with as little fuss as possible.

CHAPTER
19

THE STORY OF THE STENT 1

"STAFF: How was duty?
SWEET: Methinks you don't have to be mad to work here but
    it helps."

PETER NICHOLS The National Health

I have been discharged from the Royal Free after my five month stay, but am still suffering quite badly from nausea, acidity and gastric reflux. However, having had an endoscopy to check my stomach, I am assured that there is nothing mechanically wrong, and that the digestive problems should gradually improve as my body gets used to eating again after so many weeks of being drip-fed. My GP refers me to the excellent Palliative Care Unit at the Middlesex Hospital in order to draw on their experience of administering anti-nausea drugs; and having heard that hypnotherapy is supposed to be particularly helpful for dealing with gastric problems, I also spend several sessions at a local alternative health centre listening to a tall South African woman as she tells me in a sing-song voice that I am moving into ever deeper states of relaxation and am now able to eat without discomfort or difficulty.

If only it were that easy. Rather disappointingly, I do not think I am ever successfully hypnotized, and my symptoms actually grow worse rather than better, since I now begin to develop problems swallowing, often choking on my food as I eat. Chris, the palliative care doctor, prescribes small doses of valium and even suggests I try some pills derived from cannabis in order to help me relax, as he suspects that my problems may be caused by anxiety about eating. All this is to no avail, however – the pills are no more effective at transporting me to a light-headed realm of trouble-free meals than hypnosis. Determined not to be beaten, Chris refers me, rather bizarrely, to a unit called Speech and Language, and asks them to double-check that there is no physical cause underlying my problems. They arrange a video fluoroscopy – a kind of moving X-ray that involves the patient eating different foods coated in dye contrast – and this reveals that I do not have a psycho-logical block, but a stricture in my gullet or, to use the medical term, oesophagus. It is no longer shaped like a large-diameter hose, but bears a strong resemblance to an hour-glass, with a dramatic narrowing just above my stomach. Given the tiny aperture through which food now has to pass, it is a miracle that I am still able to swallow anything at all.

I report this discovery back to the doctors at the Royal Free, who seem rather miffed that they have not made it themselves and insist that they take their own X-ray to confirm the diagnosis. I am less than delighted at having to swallow more barium-coated food, which tastes like slightly fruit-flavoured chalk and leaves me feeling more nauseous than ever. Unsurprisingly, however, their camera tells exactly the same story as the one at the Middlesex, and so I am duly admitted to my old ward a week or two later for a further endoscopy during which, I am told, they will attempt to dilate (i.e. stretch) my oesophagus back to its proper shape.

The procedure – which involves putting a camera down the patient's throat and through the oesophagus into the stomach – is scheduled to take place after lunch, and this means I am not allowed to eat or drink anything from the time I wake up in the morning. While I wait I am asked whether I would mind two medical students exam-ining me as part of their training. I agree, and they do so with exemplary courtesy and respect. Each stage of the examination is pref-aced with an explanation about what they are doing and polite requests for my co-operation. Could I possibly raise my shirt in order for them to listen to my heart? Would I mind lying down and letting them feel my stomach? The procedure has obviously been ingrained into them as part of their training, and they have learnt their lessons well.

A few minutes after they have finished, the young houseman who is looking after me appears, looking whey-faced and embarrassed. He informs me that for some unknown reason I don't seem to be on the endoscopy list for that afternoon, and that therefore he doesn't think the procedure will now take place. I have had enough experience of bureaucratic institutions – whether it be the Royal Free or the BBC – to know that one should never accept unchallenged such vague and obstructive pronouncements. So I demand to know why, if I am not on the list, I have been called in for this appointment and just occupied a precious hospital bed for the night? I remind the young doctor of the difficulty I am having eating, and urge him to go back and query the confusion. He rather reluctantly agrees to do so, and goes away to make another phone call.

By now I am extremely hungry from not having eaten since the previous night, and my mood is grumpy and irascible. I muse bitterly on the contrast between the care and consideration that my student doctors have been taught to show, and the unthinking disregard which is the actuality of medical practice. I also reflect on the paradox that as a patient you literally entrust your life to people whom you wouldn't rely on to organize a piss-up in a brewery (an endoscopy in a hospital being presumably the medical equivalent of that).

My fuming is eventually interrupted by the houseman returning. "I've spoken to Endoscopy again," he announces uneasily. "They said they'd see what they can do, but I'm not optimistic." He seems rather ground down and unable to cope with the problem. Seven years of medical training have evidently not equipped him with the skills to deal with the insane vagaries of the hospital system.

Perhaps significantly, it is Gabriella, the colorectal nurse, who seems to unlock the situation. She is listening to my disgruntled brooding when the doctor reappears with his gloomy prognosis. An hour or so later she returns to my bedside with the news that I shall have my endoscopy that day after all. I ask her how she knows, and she tells me with a self-effacing shrug that she has been up to Endoscopy and talked to the staff about my problem. "They're very nice in there," she remarks. "They said they'd squeeze you in." A friendly but purposeful young woman with considerable hospital experience, I suspect her supportive intervention may be the reason.

So I have my endoscopy, but after all the waiting and delays it achieves little. They cannot get the camera past the stricture, and my oesophagus remains undilated. After the sedation has worn off, I am discharged with the houseman saying that he will ring and tell me what is to happen next – but that he will not be organizing it himself as he is moving to another department at the end of the week. I am not sure whether I feel relieved or frustrated at having to start the whole agonizing process with someone different. While I wait for his call, I resume my pattern of interrupted and abandoned meals. I have lost a huge amount of weight since my cancer operation, so can ill afford not to eat properly. But squeezing food through the chicane in my gullet, which becomes blocked by the tiniest of morsels, continues to be a distressing, daily struggle.

CHAPTER
20

MY DAY IN CASUALTY

"The ailing physician remains a paradox to the average mind, a questionable phenomenon."

THOMAS MANN The Magic Mountain

Someone from the Royal Free does call during the next few days, and I am told that a dilatation has now been arranged for me the following week. Unfortunately, however, there are no beds available in the hospital at that time. I am therefore instructed to present myself at Casualty on the day before the procedure is due in order to secure one of the beds that are kept for emergency cases. I am also informed that responsibility for the problem with my oesophagus is being passed from Mr Thomas, my colorectal surgeon, to Mr Jackson, who deals with thoracic cases. This is because, if the dilatation goes wrong and my oesophagus ruptures while being stretched, it is he who will have to cut through my chest and perform the emergency surgery required to repair it.

With that cheering prospect in mind, and rather bewildered at having to go to A & E to secure admission when I am clearly neither an accident nor an emergency, I make my way to the hospital on the appointed day. I explain myself to the Casualty receptionist and, after a wait of three quarters of an hour or so, am called through the swing doors into the A & E department proper. A nurse then takes down some details of my case and asks me to wait on another set of plastic seats.

People come and go all around, and eventually the Charge Nurse stops to inform me that unfortunately they are exceptionally busy. He therefore does not have a spare cubicle in which I can wait. However, if I want to lie down he can offer me a trolley parked up in the public area, opposite the main desk where ranks of doctors and other staff make their phone calls and process the patients. One of the side effects of the choking fits caused by my stricture is that they aggravate the fistula between my small bowel and the abdomen wall, causing increased and embarrassing discharges. Lying down does make things easier, so I gratefully accept the offer.

I arrived at the hospital around mid-day, and lunchtime has now come and gone. I am growing hungry. Fortunately, my sister-in-law has called in to see how I am faring and brought some sandwiches with her from a nearby supermarket. I share a plastic-packed round of prawn on brown with her and Anna as broken limbs and bandaged eyes are wheeled round us in a kind of ghostly slow-motion. I chew each mouthful with elaborate precision to try and prevent a further choking fit, but there is no need to hurry. It is well past tea-time before my trolley is shunted into a vacant cubicle.

There the Charge Nurse, who (like all charge nurses these days apparently) seems to have modelled his behaviour on Derek Thompson's performance as Charlie Fairhead in *Casualty*, asks me to change into a hospital gown. He also apologizes for the delay and tells me that I am going to be transferred to the A & E day ward where I shall be seen by a doctor.

Around 5.30pm, a porter ferries me to the ward, and two separate doctors subsequently appear and each takes my case history. Since my extensive notes are elsewhere in the building, this is not the work of moments, but once it is finished I am eventually moved from the subterranean gloom of the A & E department to an Ear, Nose and Throat ward on the sixth floor where I am to spend the night. I make it there shortly after 7pm, just in time for a late dinner, and in between fill the empty minutes reflecting on how I have put yet another dent in the government's target for all A & E patients to be seen within four hours. It gives me little satisfaction, however. The whole arcane procedure for securing admission just seems a ludicrous waste of everyone's time and energy.

CHAPTER
21

THE STORY OF THE STENT 2

"Hegel remarks somewhere that all facts and personages of great importance in world history occur, as it were, twice. He forgot to add: the first time as tragedy, the second as farce."
KARL MARX The Eighteenth Brumaire of Louis Bonaparte

The following morning the senior nurse on McLaggan Ward informs me that my dilatation has been scheduled for 2pm that afternoon, and that a member of Mr Jackson's team will visit me during the morning to explain the procedure and take me through the consent form before I sign it.

No doctor appears during the morning, but around 1.45pm the Clinical Fellow on duty (not part of Mr Jackson's "firm") comes to my bedside and announces that he believes there has been a change of plan.

"Mr Jackson has had another look at your X-rays. Apparently, he now thinks it would be safer to fit a stent rather than risk a dilatation. One of his team will come to see you shortly and explain everything. But I'm just letting you know that you probably won't be having your planned procedure this afternoon."

I begin to have a feeling of déjà vu. In anticipation of the dilatation,

I have eaten nothing all morning and am now extremely hungry. However, after my previous experience I am reluctant to abandon all hope of something happening on the basis of a second-hand message. It certainly seems foolish to pre-empt it doing so by tucking into lunch. I elect to continue hoping and not eating while waiting for the relevant doctor to arrive.

As the afternoon wears on, I give up believing that I shall have my dilatation that day, but it is well into the early evening before one of Mr Jackson's housemen comes to see me. He seems rather vague and bewildered about everything, but explains that a stent is a kind of hollow metal spring that expands into position and would permanently hold open the narrowed section of my oesophagus. Stents are also used in heart surgery to hold open collapsed arteries, and Mr Jackson feels this would be a better option than dilating my oesophagus, which might tear when stretched as it has become so emaciated. It is possible that a stent could be fitted the following day, so if I am agreeable they will keep me in overnight in order to ensure I am available and ready for that.

I accept the change of plan (what else can I do?), but I cannot help wondering why it has been made so late in the day, and whether the doctors are really "on the case". There is also a complication since the Ear, Nose and Throat ward has now become aware of my history of MRSA. Saying my bed is needed for another patient, they swiftly arrange for me to be transferred to a room of my own in Mann Ward, on the third floor next to ITU.

After breakfast the next morning, Mr Jackson's registrar comes to visit me on his rounds. Somehow I feel less than surprised when he tells me that they will not be able to fit the stent that day. He suggests that I come into their clinic the following Tuesday and see Mr Jackson himself, who will take the matter on from there. Feeling unloved and weary, but thinking this may finally produce some conclusive action, I wait until the registrar returns with an appointment time, and then set off home once again, my gullet still constricted.

CHAPTER
22

THE SURGEON'S FOOT

"The ailing physician remains a paradox to the average mind,
a questionable phenomenon."
THOMAS MANN The Magic Mountain

The next week I return to the hospital accompanied by Anna and her
mother, who happens to be staying with us. We are all ushered into a
consulting room, and, after a short pause, the door opposite opens and
Mr Jackson hobbles in, his left foot bandaged and encased in a blue
canvas stirrup.

"I'm afraid I need that seat," he tells my wife as he shepherds her
out of the chair she is sitting in and onto the consulting couch. But
having sat down, he proves to be affability itself, immediately apologiz-
ing for the confusion of the previous week.

"I was diagnosed with a melanoma on my foot on the day you were
admitted," he explains. "So when you were due to have your procedure
I was actually on the operating table myself having it removed. I'm
afraid we couldn't fit the stent on Friday because I was still recovering
and wouldn't have been able to operate on you if anything had gone
wrong."

It is a pretty convincing and disarming explanation. With my brain spinning (who's the patient here?), I simply enquire whether he is all right now?

"Oh yes, I'm back in harness," he assures me. "Though I can't trot for the moment." He then goes on to explain with admirable clarity why, after examining the X-rays again, he feels it would be preferable to fix a stent rather than risk a dilatation.

Although I do not particularly relish the idea of having a lump of coiled titanium stuck inside me for the rest of my life, his reasoning is impeccable, and the stent does have the advantage of offering a permanent solution to the problem, whereas the dilatation would need to be repeated at periodic intervals as the oesophagus shrinks back again. Mr Jackson says he will arrange with Dr Williams, the radiologist in the Specialist X-ray department who will actually fit the stent, to perform the insertion as soon as possible.

And with that we take our leave. After courteous farewells have been exchanged, Anna, her mother and I all return home rather awed and almost speechless at the bewildering, surreal turn that events have taken.

CHAPTER
23

THE STORY OF THE STENT 3

"For this relief much thanks."

WILLIAM SHAKESPEARE Hamlet

Mr Jackson is as good as his word. A week or so later, I am admitted once again to McLaggan Ward (this time by appointment rather than through A & E). Needless to say, the procedure to fit the stent is scheduled for the afternoon, and it is well after 4 pm before a porter materializes to wheel me down to the specialist X-ray suite. However, when I arrive there Dr Williams proves reassuringly efficient and well briefed, if disconcertingly young to be a consultant. He talks me through the consent form, and then successfully fits the stent, although I pass out under sedation so know little about it. The following few days are pretty uncomfortable as I retch and belch while my gullet adjusts to having this rigid foreign body permanently stuck inside it. But the problems gradually settle, and I am eventually discharged, once more able to eat without choking.

CHAPTER
24

THE STORY OF THE STENT 4

"Some people are under the impression that all that is required to make a good fisherman is the ability to tell lies easily and without blushing; but this is a mistake."

JEROME K JEROME Three Men in a Boat

Whatever my other problems with food, for six months after the insertion of my stent I am at least able to eat without choking. However, in the autumn of 2004 I am forced to return again to the Royal Free, this time for the operation to repair the fistula leaking through my abdomen wall. Unsurprisingly, given my previous experience, I feel fairly anxious about this, but the operation proves largely successful and without unexpected side effects. At least to begin with…

About a month after being discharged, I notice that once again I am starting to have difficulty swallowing. I contact Mr Jackson, who promptly arranges a chest X-ray for me, and an appointment to see him. When we meet, he tells me in a very matter of fact way that, as I know, a stent was inserted into a good position in my oesophagus earlier in the year. "The problem is that the stent's become dislodged. The X-ray shows it's no longer in your oesophagus, but sitting inside your stomach."

Without pausing for breath or any reaction from me, he continues: "As I see it, there are three possible courses of action. The first is to put a camera down into your stomach and try to fish the stent out endoscopically. If that fails, we could just leave the stent where it is, but that runs the risk of it slipping from its current position and blocking the exit from your stomach into the intestine. The third option is to remove the stent surgically, but that would mean a serious and unpleasant operation which involves cutting through the stomach wall to access it."

I leave the room reeling. The comedy of errors that constitutes the story of my stent is continuing, but it no longer seems very funny. Having learnt the hard way that one should not always expect the best or easiest outcome from any form of medical intervention, I fear that a major operation will be the only solution to the problem. I am cast into a mood of deep depression, not least because I have now been told that before they can even try retrieving the stent endoscopically the doctors will first have to dilate my oesophagus in order to pass the camera down into my stomach. A procedure that was rejected six months ago as too risky (it involves inserting a balloon into the straitened section of the oesophagus and then slowly inflating it to stretch the oesophagus temporarily well beyond its normal diameter) has now apparently become an essential preliminary to a dubious fishing expedition. If successful, and the stent is "hooked", this will then involve dragging the offending lump of metal back through a passageway that currently seems to become blocked by even tiny pieces of food.

Nevertheless, fishing the stent out is clearly the preferable solution. And so, buoyed up by the exhortations of friends and family to be optimistic rather than fear the worst, I check back into the hospital some ten days before Christmas. When I am taken down to Specialist X-ray (late in the afternoon, needless to say), I am heartened to discover that the estimable Dr Williams, who inserted the stent and has dealt with me on a number of other occasions, will be in charge of the procedure.

He greets me with slight embarrassment, saying that he doesn't know how the stent could have become dislodged since, apart from the tension of its self-expanding spring mechanism, it was also held in place by a couple of small hooks.

"I think it was probably knocked out of place during my last operation in September," I reply. "I had a naso-gastric tube and God knows what else stuck down my throat, so it would hardly be surprising."

Dr Williams pauses uneasily for a moment, clearly torn between relief that his own handiwork has not been to blame and a contradictory desire not to suggest that his colleagues have perhaps been at fault. "Look, I'm not interested in recriminations," I add in an attempt to ease the situation. "I'm not trying to find someone to blame. I just think it's by far the most likely explanation, given that my problems started again after the operation."

"You may well be right," Dr Williams eventually says by way of response, before going on to inform me that he is only able to perform the preliminary dilatation himself, and that the endoscopic part of the proceedings will require a machine to be brought down from the tenth floor and a different doctor, expert in its use, to operate it.

"I'm afraid that level of co-ordination will probably be beyond this place today," he adds wryly. "But I'll do the dilatation anyway. And I think I can organize the combined procedure to fish out the stent for the day after tomorrow."

He evidently understands how to galvanize the lumbering mechanics of the system, so that is in due course what happens. The dilatation, although quite painful, goes without mishap, and 48 hours later Dr Peters and his machine from the Endoscopy department join Dr Williams and myself in the X-ray suite. During the intervening period, I grapple with the fact that when I was admitted for my initial endoscopy nearly a year before, I was told that my oesophagus might be dilated as part of that procedure. Now I have learnt that oesophageal dilatations are performed by completely different people in a wholly separate part of the hospital. It is a bewildering discovery that makes the basis of my original admission seem even more dubious and confused than it did at the time.

However, as I wait for the fun and games to start I take consolation from the fact that experts from both the relevant departments are now on my case. The two doctors confer briefly, then admit that this is not a regular procedure they are about to undertake, and that it will therefore entail a considerable element of "try and see". Although I like and have confidence in both men, this seems less than entirely reassuring; but fortunately I am not awake to see their improvised double-act. The pethidine I am given as sedation knocks me out completely. When I come round a little while later, I am given the welcome news that Christmas has come early for me. The doctors have succeeded in fishing the stent out of my stomach. Apparently, it was covered in green slime, and they kindly held it up for me to look at. I never see it, but it is still by far the best present I receive during the yuletide festivities that year.

CHAPTER
25

EATING

"To wish me a hearty appetite is about the same as saying
'Merry Christmas' on 15 August or 'Goodnight' in broad
daylight. In the last eight months I have swallowed nothing
save a few drops of lemon-flavoured water and one half-
teaspoon of yoghurt."

JEAN-DOMINIQUE BAUBY The Diving-Bell and the Butterfly

Twice each day patients at the Royal Free are given printed menus on
which they have to tick boxes to order their meals for the day following. One of the dishes featured regularly – particularly on Fridays – is
the intriguingly named "Battered Cod".

Looking at the dense, tasteless, off-white lump of fish wrapped in a
soggy, pale-yellow film of heavy pancake that ticking this box produces
on my plate, I have repeatedly been struck by the wit of this description.
Suggesting a sympathetic kinship with battered wives rather than the
gastronomic delights of traditional fish and chips, it seems a perfect epi-
thet, and says everything that needs to be said about hospital food.

Eating is so much part of our daily routine that we tend to take it for granted – until, that is, circumstances contrive to deny us its simple pleasures. For the past three months I have been fed exclusively by drip. Not a mouthful of food has passed my lips during the whole of that time. Now, as I grow slightly stronger and my five-month stay in hospital gradually draws towards a conclusion, I demand precise details from Anna when she comes to visit of meals that she has eaten. I take immense vicarious pleasure in a plate of ham and eggs with sauté potatoes that she has enjoyed with a friend at our local gastropub. I am thrilled by her descriptions of eating fusilli in a rich pesto sauce at a nearby Ligurian restaurant, and I start to nurture fantasies about the dinner parties I shall prepare for friends when I finally make it home from hospital. Alas, when I am allowed to eat again I find that my stomach is no longer able to cope with many sorts of food, and that my tastebuds have developed some unwelcome sensitivities. Wine, when I eventually come to drink it, has the sour, sharp flavour I remember from when I first sampled it as an adolescent. Tap water, at my in-laws in Cornwall, I find undrinkable owing to the strong taste of chlorine. Vegetables, such as peas or asparagus, simply race straight through my system and reduce it to water. I cannot even face eating chocolate without feeling nauseous. Various friends have brought me Easter eggs by way of seasonal gifts when visiting, but these sit by my bedside untouched.

■ ■ ■

Shortly after I resume eating, the Royal Free has a revolution in its catering procedures as part of a government programme to improve hospital food. Instead of being served in compartmentalized plastic trays like bad airline meals, dishes are now re-heated in trolleys on the wards and then portioned out by the nursing staff, who don special blue plastic aprons for the purpose. Having been decorously arranged on proper china plates, the meals are then ferried to the waiting patients, who all receive personal salt and pepper pots along with their food to crown the sense of gourmet eating. This change has the welcome result of filling the wards with tantalizing smells of cooking at lunch and dinner times, and many is the occasion after it has been introduced that I sit, forbidden to eat because of some impending procedure, and find myself taunted by the wafting aromas of meals about to be served. Sadly, however, the promise is far superior to the delivery, because, whatever the improvement in presentation, the meals themselves remain unchanged. It is still tired meat and over-cooked vegetables that appear on the plates, battered cod followed by sugary whips for dessert.

Returning to the hospital recently for an overnight stay, I arrive on the ward, as requested, just in time for dinner. Based on much experi-ence, I decide that roast lamb with mint sauce and mashed potato is the safest choice among the options available. But when it arrives, the fatty slices of lamb – always a distant relation to the meat that passes by that name elsewhere – is covered by a heavy puddle of mucous-like gravy; the mashed potato is lumpy; and there is no mint sauce to disguise the flavour – they have run out. The meal looks, and tastes, inedible.

■ ■ ■

There has been considerable concern and publicity about hospital food in recent years. Statistics concerning untouched meals and wasted resources shed little light on the matter, however, since patients recov-ering from surgery, or who are simply unwell, do not have normal appetites. But there is clearly a problem, and the quality of hospital food is part of it, since for the most part it remains abysmal.

The difficulty of course – as with "Jamie's School Dinners" – is to a large extent financial. Apparently, in the NHS £2.50 is spent on catering for each patient per day. That makes the £1.50 to £1.70 for the average school lunch look positively generous. If Jamie Oliver struggles to make one decent meal for that figure – which includes the princely sum of 37p for ingredients – then what chance has the average hospital chef of providing a wholesome breakfast, lunch and dinner each day for little more than half as much again? No wonder the cod is battered. Trying to work within these constraints would drive any chef to violence.

■ ■ ■

Owing to a shortage of beds, I spend one of my many nights at the Royal Free on Gloucester Ward – the hospital's private wing. There I enjoy, but without having to pay for the privilege, a private room with wooden rather than linoleum flooring; a full-size television; a clean bathroom; and the unfussed attention of the nursing staff who seem considerably less stressed than their counterparts on the public wards. I also discover – with some perverse pleasure it must be admitted – that the food served to the hospital's private patients is, with one small difference, exactly the same as that offered to its NHS ones. The difference is that private patients can have croissants for breakfast instead of sliced bread or toast. However, despite the hospital's location in Hampstead, with its plethora of continental tea-rooms and fine bakers, the croissants on offer are no better than supermarket quality. I do not end my stay wishing that I could return next time as a private patient on account of the culinary and nutritional advantages.

■ ■ ■

The sad fact is, despite the growing awareness of the importance of food and diet for good health, nutrition remains a low priority within the medical profession. Faced with my post-operative problems of acidity, nausea and weight loss, the surgeon, Mr Thomas – a talented, hard-working man – prescribes anti-reflux drugs to deal with the discomfort, counsels patience in the belief that things will eventually "settle down", and refers me to the hospital's team of dieticians to advise me about eating.

I was a fairly slim 11 stones when admitted to hospital; by the time I am ready to be discharged I weigh just seven stones and look like a concentration camp survivor. Confronted by this, the nutritionists feel I should ignore the normal rules of healthy eating and simply gorge myself on carbohydrates. Burgers and chips, ice cream, sticky buns, bacon and eggs: if I fancy them, then eat them is what I am told, and the more fattening the better. The dieticians also instruct me to eat or drink food supplements, and prescribe a disgusting range of mostly milk-based drinks packed with added calories and protein.

The problem is that most of these supplements make me feel – and in some cases be – violently sick. I am consequently reluctant to take them. The diet "experts" respond with patronising sulkiness, treating me like a naughty schoolboy who simply doesn't know what's good for him and refuses to eat his greens. I do not fare a great deal better with the lashings of carbohydrates either. Even small platefuls of fish and chips or cream cake generally leave me feeling bloated and acutely indigested. Nevertheless, I do my utmost to gain weight. I take to eating cooked breakfasts; I devour as much meat and fish as I can possibly manage in order to keep up my protein intake; I eat biscuits and cheese at elevenses; and I feast on cake and crumpets for tea.

Although I suffer for it, initially this regime seems to have some effect. Three months after leaving hospital, my weight has crept back up to eight stones. But there it stops and stubbornly remains, whatever else I devour. And if I eat the wrong thing – too much Christmas pudding, for instance – that upsets my stomach and sends my weight crashing back below seven and a half stones, requiring many more weeks of painstaking effort to reclaim the lost ground. I also continue to be plagued by nausea and acidity, with frequent belching fits and bouts of feeling intensely sick.

The complications of my case seem to leave the hospital dieticians at a loss. My problems with acidity suggest that I should perhaps follow a more alkaline diet and eat less meat and dairy produce; but I need to keep up my protein intake to assist the post-operative healing process (my surgical wound has still not fully knitted and continues to ooze bloody discharges). Heavy, calorific foods leave me feeling uncomfortable; lighter and more conventionally healthy ones, such as brown rice and most vegetables, are more than my ileostomy is able to cope with and race through my system like a jet-propelled scourer, leaving no opportunity for any nutrients to be absorbed. I clearly do not conform to the dieticians' protocols, or fit the limited experience that they can bring to bear. I see several different advisers, but in each case find that the quality of the recommendations they are making is simply unequal to the task. In no way does it seem comparable to the expertise that I have found elsewhere in the hospital system.

So, after 18 months with no further weight gain and constant digestive discomfort that culminates in a depressing trip to France during which most of my meals prove an ordeal rather than a pleasure, I eventually take myself off – at considerable expense and after a long search to find her, for she had not yet been given her own television series – to a private doctor based near Harley Street who specializes in nutrition. Dr Denning's initial response to my problems is to say that she thinks she can help with the nausea and indigestion, but that she is less sure how much she can contribute in terms of weight gain, certainly as long as my ileostomy remains in place. It proves a fair, if cautious, prognosis. After running some blood tests, she identifies that I am suffering from a serious deficiency of B vitamins (which are needed to metabolise food), and proposes that I take supplements and have injections to boost these. She suggests that I try stopping my daily dose of reflux drugs (which by this time I have been taking for almost two years) and, after examining a food diary that she asks me to keep, makes some relatively simple recommendations concerning diet: that I avoid mixing protein and carbohydrates with fruit and sweet desserts at the same meal; that I avoid fried foods: and that I watch (i.e. moderate) my intake of fats and sugars. She also advises me to eat less! (Or at least to avoid bloating myself in a futile attempt to gain weight).

Dropping the acidity pills seems to make no appreciable difference to my well-being (so why have I been taking them I wonder?); but the other innovations she proposes most certainly do. Within a week or two I find I am far less uncomfortable after meals, and therefore much less tired simply from the effort of digesting my food. I gradually grow less nauseous and find I have more energy. As a result I am able to be more active, and start to exercise more. That in turn stimulates my appetite, and I begin to rebuild my wasted muscles. After three or four months I notice that I am even starting to gain a little weight, and have breached my eight stone ceiling.

It would be an exaggeration to suggest that my problems disappear entirely. I am still a long way from how I was before I went into hospital. However, the change is profound, and the progress ongoing. After more than a year under the guidance of Dr Denning, my weight continues to creep upwards. Almost everything that she has proposed by way of tests, remedies and supplements is available within the NHS (though I think the health service might draw the line at offering Oil of Oregano on prescription). However, neither the dieticians nor anyone else inside the state system has had the knowledge, interest or wit to suggest them. My doctors were more than happy to prescribe any number of antacid and anti-sickness drugs in the attempt to find ones that worked. But none did, and in doing so they only ever addressed the symptoms of my case, never the causes of the problem.

CHAPTER
26

SIDE EFFECTS

"I am home and resting, but what I am resting from is not cancer. I am resting from an illness caused by an illness caused by curing cancer."

> JOHN DIAMOND *Snake Oil and Other Preoccupations*, 'Iatrogenesis'

When Anna was pregnant with our first child, I read a number of books about becoming a parent, and remember being a little daunted by the statistics they contained. An alarmingly high number of pregnancies would end in miscarriage (well, we already had experience of that); one or two per cent of babies would suffer from this defect or that fatal disease; another small percentage would die in childbirth; some would have Down's Syndrome (more likely if, like Anna, the mother was over 30 and thus an "elderly *prima gravida*"); others would have to contend with cerebral palsy. Adding all these figures together, I soon began to think it a miracle that any of us survived at all. However, I took comfort from the fact that when friends became pregnant, although their labours were often difficult, ranging from breech births to caesarean and forceps deliveries, they invariably seemed to emerge from the ordeal radiantly happy, if a little bruised, and with healthy "normal" babies. And so it was with us. Adam came out as a strapping, if eye-watering, nine and a half pounder. But there was a slight sting in the tail, for I fear the whole experience may have lulled me into a false sense of security when it came to dealing with hospitals for very different reasons later.

One of the rituals you have to go through before almost any medical procedure nowadays is signing a consent form. Whether it is major bowel surgery or a routine colonoscopy, a doctor will talk you through the proposed treatment and tell you the risks that the operation or other intervention may involve. You have the opportunity to ask questions and raise any concerns you may feel, and then, once you are happy, you sign a form agreeing to what may be done to your body.

The principle behind this routine is a sound one, but all too often it becomes an empty formality that is more about the hospital protecting itself legally than informing or empowering the patient. This is partly because the task of obtaining consent is frequently given to junior doctors to perform, and they have no more real knowledge of the risks involved in the planned procedure than the patient. The dangers outlined are merely a learnt list of possible complications, not anything of which the doctor has first-hand experience. Not surprisingly, therefore, he or she may be unable to answer many of the questions that the patient wishes to raise.

The other problem is that trying to give an accurate or balanced sense of the danger inherent in any procedure is actually extremely difficult. It is certainly not something that can properly be done – as often tends to be the case – as the patient is wheeled into the investigation suite or operating theatre with an entire medical team expectantly standing by and waiting to spring into action. In consequence, and also to ensure that patients are not reduced to quivering wrecks before they submit to the anaesthetic, the risks are usually played down. The doctor races through them rather like a safety briefing before a flight: a requirement that has to be complied with, but nothing to worry about or even pay much attention to. In a detail which says everything about how the whole ritual is regarded, staff will ask not, "Have you signed a consent form?" or even, "Have you given your consent?", but *"Have you been consented?"* With one casual and tiny massacre of the English language, the patient's autonomy is effortlessly stripped away.

The single meaningful action that he or she is able to perform in this context – agreeing to the proposed treatment – is denied as grammar is destroyed and the verb "to consent" is rendered nonsensically passive. Consenting is apparently not something you do, but, like everything in hospital, something that is done to you. It hardly suggests that the practice is being taken seriously or that the formality is a meaningful one.

While I was not oblivious to the risks of surgery, I must admit that, led on by the doctors' example, l tended to regard them in much the same way as one views the risks of flying or of childbirth – not to be entirely discounted but sufficiently remote as not to be worth worrying about. I should have realized that performing surgery is perhaps more like making a film than piloting a plane, and remembered my cardinal rule as a producer: always expect the unexpected. The problems are never where you think they are going to be. So in the same way that when I nervously committed to a star actor with a reputation for being difficult, and then discovered working with him to be a delight, only to have the production almost come unstuck because the actor cast opposite him was inexplicably refused a work permit, the complications following surgery that Anna and I experienced were neither ones we fearfully anticipated, nor ones of which we had been forewarned.

No one ever mentioned fistulas as a possible side effect of bowel surgery in advance of Anna's operation. However, when she subsequently discovered that she was losing blood rectally during menstruation, the creation of a fistula was immediately proffered as the most likely reason. When no fistula could be found, the doctors were stumped for an explanation and rather doubtfully suggested that the misplaced bleeding might be the result of endometrial seeds being dislodged during surgery. It was a possible but less than entirely convincing theory. It was certainly not a side effect that anyone had anticipated.

The side effects of chemotherapy are, however, well known – indeed, it is for these that the term "iatrogenic illness" (that is, illness caused by medical examination or treatment, from the Greek word *iatros*, meaning physician) might have been invented. Anna was fortunate in that her course of treatment was preventative rather than curative, and therefore relatively mild. It did not involve hair-loss or any of the other more unpleasant consequences of pumping your body full of toxic chemicals. Nevertheless, it did mean – as we were fore-warned – that for two days each week following the infusion of drugs she felt nauseous and exhausted. It also meant that after nearly six months of treatment she began to experience anticipatory sickness before the infusions as well. This was not a development her oncolo-gist had specifically prepared us for, but it was clearly neither unusual nor unexpected.

What was much less foreseen was that in the years following her chemotherapy, Anna would experience recurrent bouts of extreme fatigue accompanied by other viral symptoms, such as aching lymph glands. Despite a barrage of tests, her various doctors struggled to come up with a definite explanation for this, but it did seem to be related to a low white blood-cell count that the investigations revealed. One of the undesired effects of chemotherapy is that it destroys white blood cells, so it is natural to wonder whether her susceptibility to viral symptoms might not be a long-term consequence of her cancer treat-ment. The doctors are sceptical, but finally non-commital on the subject.

■ ■ ■

Whatever the side effects Anna experienced – anticipated or otherwise – they are as nothing compared to the precipitous chain of events that my own surgery sets in motion. Before my first bowel re-section, I am in ostensibly good health. I have not seen a doctor for several years, am energetic and reasonably fit, and the only symptom of my nascent cancer is a tiny trace of rectal bleeding which my GP had thought was most probably caused by piles. It is therefore a cause of surprise and bafflement to everyone when, in the days following my surgery, my ileostomy stops working and my temperature starts to soar. I am pre-scribed Ibuprofen to bring it down, but this causes – or certainly is followed by, and it is a known side effect of the drug – internal bleed-ing in my stomach. This takes the form, not of some invisible, internal leakage, but of spectacular vomiting. There is a scene in one of Ken Russell's musical biographies where the consumptive Chopin coughs up blood over the keys of the piano on which he is composing. Messy though this is, his effusion is tiny compared with the mighty flood of dark red liquid that I manage to bring up over the hospital floor as I lie down for some procedure. I am rushed off for an endoscopy that reveals massive internal haemorrhaging, which the doctors struggle for several days to staunch. It is not until I have almost died that a large dose of an extremely expensive drug called Factor VII finally brings the problem under control. In the meantime, or possibly beforehand – time has no meaning for me during all this and I am unconscious for much of it – I am taken back to the operating theatre for a further section of suspect tissue to be removed from my bowel. As a result of either this or the previous operation, however, I contract MRSA and, almost certainly as a consequence of that, subsequently develop pneumonia.

After six weeks of being drip-fed in Intensive Care, my condition has stabilized and I am finally able to return to an ordinary ward. However, I have lost four stones in weight, and am so weak that I can only walk with the aid of a zimmer frame. I have also developed the problematic fistula at the site of my abdominal wound and, following accepted practice in an attempt to allow this to heal itself, I therefore continue to be drip-fed for a further six weeks. When the doctors allow me to start eating again, my stomach has been so damaged that every meal causes indigestion. I also suffer from intense nausea. Drugs are prescribed to assist with this but bring little relief, and then I wake up one morning – the day in fact when I am due to go home for a few hours to try and prepare for my eventual discharge – with an acute pain below my right-hand ribs, an ultrasound examination reveals that this is caused by inflammation of the gall-bladder – which is one of the known side effects of prolonged periods of TPN (drip) feeding. I am prescribed antibiotics to relieve this, which in turn (as antibiotics generally do) add to my feelings of nausea.

I begin to feel like I am playing some infernal game of medical pinball in which I am the ball. As I drift towards oblivion, a timely flick on the flippers from the doctors sends me racing upwards again, only for me to crash into a cunningly concealed barrier from which I bounce off in a different direction, slap bang into a further wall that catapults me downhill once more. I long for the endless, head-spinning sequence of treatments to cease, but every time my condition seems to settle and improve a little, a further investigation or change of drugs sends me cascading backwards again. My testicles swell up to the size of a grapefruit, but I have no idea what causes this. I only remember it takes more antibiotics and concomitant nausea to return them to normal.

Sadly, even after I am discharged the chain reaction that my operation sparked continues its inexorable logic. I begin to experience the swallowing difficulties that are subsequently ascribed to a stricture in my oesophagus. This, it is thought, is the result of tissue damage, caused by excessive acidity caused by stomach damage caused by treating the fever caused by complications caused by the operation to cure my cancer. The stricture is now treated by regular oesophageal dilatations that require not eating for 24 hours, which invariably upsets the fragile balance my stomach has attained and results in a few days of renewed nausea and discomfort following each procedure.

It is relatively small beer, but it offers a repeated reminder of three things that I have developed or learnt as a result of my experiences. The first is an intense yearning to be free of hospitals and to take as few drugs as possible. Every intervention or course of pills carries its own set of consequences. The waters become muddied, and you are left fumbling ever more helplessly to identify your baseline symptoms and understand the true cause of your problems. Only by escaping hospital procedures for significant periods and resisting the temptation of increasing chemical reliance does it seem possible to break the relentless cycle of side effects and complications that prevents any sustained progress or feeling of improvement.

The second thing I have learnt is a sense of the body's wholeness, of the connectedness of its different parts. It functions as a totality, or not at all. You cannot view organs in isolation, as damaged parts which may simply be repaired or renewed. Treat a disease in one place and you inevitably affect the whole – the intervention has implications for the entire body. A mechanistic, compartmentalized approach to medicine, still so common in Western practice, is fundamentally flawed and inadequate for the task.

Finally, I have come to realize the risk or danger involved in any medical treatment. Because the body works as a whole, you interfere with its fantastically subtle, self-regulating balance at your peril. Even something as routine as a CT scan has consequences that the body can take several days to "correct". This is not an argument for avoiding treatment, but it is one for agreeing to nothing lightly. I have always found cosmetic surgery hard to understand, but I now find it simply incomprehensible. Any non-essential operation involves risks that do not seem worth taking. Doctors who are administering treatments and prescribing drugs every day can easily become blasé about the cost to the patient. They also tend not to tell the full story about the risks involved because they do not wish to cause alarm and prompt the patient to refuse the intervention.

When Anna was prescribed chemotherapy, a doctor friend lent me a medical journal that contained some recent research into alternative forms of adjuvant therapy. Regrettably, the most successful of these were still only at trial stage, but what struck home for me were the sobering statistics that the article revealed on survival rates for people with bowel cancer. For patients with Anna's particular form of the disease, a paltry 43 per cent could expect to live for five years or more following surgery. With "preventative" chemotherapy, this figure rose to around 57 per cent. These were less than encouraging odds either way, but on the basis that for every five people with the disease at least two were going to die anyway, and a third would follow suit if chemotherapy were not prescribed and accepted, there was no way that it made sense to refuse the treatment, whatever the side effects – known or unknown. But having said that, I certainly do not think that my grandfather's lifelong determination to avoid going anywhere near a hospital was without its own, grimly-learnt, wisdom.

CHAPTER
27

CURTAINS

"I have often thought since, that she must have looked as if the admission of the natural light of day would have struck her to dust."

CHARLES DICKENS Great Expectations

The curtains that surround the beds in Cordwainers' Ward and in most of the other wards in the Royal Free (the fabric must have been bought as a job lot) are covered in drawings of well-known landmarks from around the world. The pattern comprises a montage of pastel-coloured sketches depicting such tourist icons as Big Ben, the Sydney Opera House, the Golden Gate Bridge and the Great Wall of China. There are images of the Rialto and a gondola from Venice, the Leaning Tower of Pisa and Gaudi's Sagrada Familia in Barcelona.

In the absence of much else to look at, I spend many hours staring at these familiar sights, lost in the thoughts and memories they provoke. As my temperature soars and my condition deteriorates, I recognize the gravity of my situation with the realization that I shall now probably never visit Sydney and see the rippling fins of the Opera

House in the flesh. I also become fixated by the burgeoning domes of Sacré-Coeur in Paris.

This extraordinary basilica that looms before me was built as the result of a vow made during the Franco-Prussian War in 1870 to erect a monument of thanksgiving if Paris were spared destruction. Against fearful expectations it was, and building soon started to honour the bargain with Providence, although ironically the edifice was only completed in 1919 after liberation from a further war with Germany in which the French capital was once again threatened.

As I lie in bed, looking feverishly at this towering act of propitiation, I make my own vow: namely, that if I am spared destruction and survive to do so, I will visit Paris and make a pilgrimage to Sacré-Coeur as my own small act of thanksgiving.

■ ■ ■

It is early June 2003. After five months in hospital, I go to stay with my parents in Buckinghamshire for a few days as part of my convalescence. It proves a curious visit. My mother, who is normally busy about the house, cooking, cleaning and tidying, seems to have relinquished most of these duties to my father, who has previously taken a fairly passive role on the domestic front, especially since having a heart attack some three or four years before. My mother escorts me on short walks along their bungalow-lined crescent, but otherwise spends most of the time resting. She has also developed a slight obsession with closing the curtains if the sun comes out and is shining into the room. This is something she has always done, supposedly to protect the carpets from fading and keep the house cool, but she does it now with unprecedented rigour. Even the gentlest evening rays are promptly shut out, and curtains drawn on windows that admit no direct sunlight whatsoever.

It is a beautiful summer, and I hate the habit, wanting to enjoy as much of the glorious sunshine as possible. So I sneak round after her, opening little gaps to let in the daylight. When I return home my parents pay a visit to me, and, as soon as the sun comes out, my mother starts to draw the curtains in our flat. But in my own home I feel I can reasonably object, and so use my proprietorial rights to insist that they are opened again. After five months of being incarcerated in hospital, the last thing I want to do is shut myself off from the world outside and retreat into my own sheltered, shadowy space.

A month later, my mother is diagnosed as having ovarian cancer. This explains her listlessness when I visited, and marks the start of a rapid physical decline. I go to see her as often as my limited strength will allow, and on one of my trips I am gutted to see how the person who took me out for walks only a few weeks previously is now wasted and bed-bound. I have lost weight and still look emaciated, but my mother is like a skeleton, the skin on her face stretched so tight that her skull seems to be showing through.

There has been a problem with the garage door of my parents' bungalow, and at the time of this visit a replacement one has recently been delivered. For want of a better place to leave it until it is fitted, the door has been leant over the window of the bedroom where my mother is lying, which is adjacent to the garage. The enormous door is like a solid curtain and makes the room horribly dark, so that the electric light has to be switched on the whole time. But my mother does not seem to notice or be bothered by it.

Three days later – in the same darkened room – she dies.

■ ■ ■

Immediately after my release from hospital, I feel unable to step out of doors without someone accompanying me. Recovery proves slow, painful and erratic, but after two years I finally feel strong enough to consider travelling abroad again. Some friends offer us the use of an apartment on the Giudecca in Venice, and in the summer of 2005 I sail under the Rialto Bridge aboard a vaporetto. In the autumn of the same year, I go to Paris for a few days and make my pilgrimage to Sacré-Coeur, where I slowly climb the steep hill to the cathedral and light a candle of thanksgiving. The human spirit – or human folly – being what it is, I also start to dream about visiting Sydney to see the Opera House.

CHAPTER
28

SIGNS AND MEANINGS

"Of course, one cannot think without metaphors. But that does not mean there aren't some metaphors we might well abstain from or try to retire."

SUSAN SONTAG AIDS and Its Metaphors

The word "hospital" is a medieval invention derived from the Latin *hospes* meaning host or, paradoxically, guest. The term thus has its roots in the realm of hospitality, and hospitals were originally places of shelter or refuge for pilgrims and travellers. Subsequently, the word was applied to charitable institutions, usually connected to religious orders, which took in the needy and cared for them. Vestiges of this older meaning survive in the proper names, Christ's Hospital School (founded 1552) and Thomas Coram's Foundling Hospital (established 1739). Neither of these were ever medical foundations (indeed the Foundling Hospital only admitted infants who were in good health), but both institutions housed and looked after poor and abandoned children.

However, part of the Christian commitment to showing compassion for the needy was nursing the sick, aged and infirm, and so hospitals gradually took on a medical role. The hospital founded in

Jerusalem around 1048 by merchants from Amalfi, for instance, was originally for the purpose of housing poor pilgrims, but it later became the home of the Knights Hospitallers, an order of monks dedicated to the care of the sick and infirm. Formally known as the Knights of the Hospital of St John of Jerusalem, they subsequently moved their chief seat to Malta, renamed themselves the Knights of Malta, and became the inspiration for the St John's Ambulance Brigade.

In England, St Bartholomew's and St Thomas's Hospitals were established in 1123 and around 1215 respectively as religious houses providing charitable care for the sick. But although their work embraced a medical dimension, they were more like hospices than hospitals in contemporary terms, offering nursing support rather than specialized treatment. The words "hospice" and "hostel" share the same semantic root as hospital, and both give a better guide to the nature of these medieval institutions than the word hospital itself with its contemporary connotations.

During the medieval period also, a number of specialized leper asylums were built, where "unclean" leprosy sufferers could be safely housed away from the rest of the population, or even forcibly confined. By 1225, there were some 19,000 of these leprosaria spread across Europe, and as leprosy declined many were requisitioned for people suspected of carrying other infectious diseases, the insane, or even the vagrant poor. In the 14th century, when bubonic plague struck, leprosaria were also turned into the first plague hospitals. In several different ways, these buildings thus began the use of hospitals for incarceration, and forged the first of many curious links between hospitals and prisons.

Most evidently these are seen in mental hospitals, where patients seldom stay entirely voluntarily. In London, the hospital of St Mary of Bethlem began to care for the sick in mind during the 14th century, and its nine inmates in 1403 steadily grew in number as "Bedlam" became established as England's first (and for many years only) lunatic asylum. "Treatment" consisted of forcible restraint: one inventory lists "six chains with locks and keys belonging to them, four pairs of iron manacles, five other chains of iron and two pairs of stocks" among the hospital's possessions.

In 17th century France, this blurring of the boundaries between caring and constraining was extended as the *hôpital général* became established throughout the country as an institution designed to shelter – and confine – beggars, orphans, vagabonds, prostitutes and thieves alongside the sick and insane. The poorhouse emerged in England during the century following to fulfil a similar function; and at that time, under the French system of justice, reclusion in hospital served as the equivalent punishment for women that banishment abroad on convict galleys was for men.

As imprisonment gradually became the legal system's dominant form of punishment, those at the forefront of prison reform also frequently led moves for the reform of hospitals, which were regarded at the time as gateways to death, rife with infection, rather than as the life-saving institutions we like to view them as today. The philanthropist John Howard drafted the 1779 Act of Parliament which brought the idea onto the statute book that the purpose of prison was not simply to punish, but to reform the soul and change conduct. He subsequently turned his attention to the remodelling of hospitals, insisting on the need for cleanliness and fresh air to combat the deadly miasmic effluvia which he and others blamed for the shocking mortality of both hospitals and jails. Elizabeth Fry, who worked and campaigned vigorously for the improvement of prison conditions, particularly for women, in the early 19th century, went on to seek ways of raising the standards of nursing in hospitals. Inspired by a visit to the Deaconess Institute in Germany, she founded the Institute of Nursing on her return to London in 1840, and this later became the inspiration for Florence Nightingale when she sought to establish a nurses' training scheme after the Crimean War.

As the French thinker Michel Foucault outlines in his extraordinary book *Discipline and Punish*, the modern, "clinical" hospital came into being at the same time that the prison emerged in its contemporary guise as the primary form of legal punishment. One was aimed at the curing of physical diseases. The other, using similar techniques of isolation, observation and careful discipline, was aimed at curing moral ones, and sought to turn delinquents into "healthy" citizens. Foucault details a host of parallels between the two institutions (and others such as schools and factories). These range from architecture – both types of building are concerned not with being seen, nor with the views out, but with internal observation – to the importance of routine and timetables, and a shared emphasis on the precise documentation of individual "cases".

It is less than surprising then that, in the quotes given earlier in this book, both Chekhov and Solzhenitsyn should suggest a similarity between hospitals and prisons; or that when the Location Manager and Designer of my first television production were seeking a plausible interior to serve as Harmondsworth Detention Centre for asylum seekers in west London, they should find it in a disused hospital in Wandsworth (a location which, incidentally, also provided convincing backstage offices at Heathrow, thus confirming another regularly drawn comparison).

The link between hospitals and prisons is also found in the use of the word "confinement" to describe a woman's retreat to bed for childbirth, or even more significantly in the meaning of "ward". This word is derived from a group of German and Old Norse words meaning to watch or guard, and long before it was used to describe a room in a hospital served as a term for a prison, or a separate division within a prison. Although this sense of the word is now obsolete, traces of its former meaning live on in the contemporary idea of a "warder".

So when we talk of a "hospital ward", we are actually describing a battleground. The phrase is a kind of oxymoron in which two conflicting ideas come face to face: on the one hand a place of rest and refuge, a source of benign hospitality; on the other a place of incarceration and constraint, a cell for oppressive confinement. It expresses the confusion, or at least the dialectic – a clash of innocence and experience – which lies at the heart of our medical institutions. But as William Blake wrote, "Without contraries is no progression", and it is out of this historical contradiction that the modern hospital has been created. With the advent of clinical medicine in the early 19th century, the emphasis gradually shifted from caring and confinement to curing; and subsequent advances in anaesthesia allied with the conquest of infection meant that surgery flourished, and hospitals – where surgery was now performed – were no longer associated with spreading infection, but became the lavishly-funded centres for treatment of the sick that we know them as today. The shelter or prison was transformed into the home of the most advanced medical practice and the salvation of the seriously ill.

Interestingly, though, the Royal Free now seems reluctant to call itself a hospital. The newly-installed sign behind the desk in its main entrance hall reads simply:

Royal Free Hampstead
NHS Trust
Reception

■ ■ ■

In his book *Non-Places: Introduction to the Anthropology of Supermodernity*, French academic Marc Augé attempts to define the characteristics of the anonymous spaces in which we spend increasing parts of our lives – "the ones we inhabit when we are driving down the motorway, wandering through the supermarket or sitting in the airport lounge". Prominent among these is the fact that in these places:

> "The link between individuals and their surroundings is
> established through the mediation of words or even texts...the
> injunctions, advice, commentaries and 'messages' transmitted
> by the innumerable 'supports' (signboards, screens, posters)
> that form an integral part of the contemporary landscape."

In common with most other hospitals, the reception area of the Royal Free is awash with electronic information boards, ward lists, directional signs, exhortatory public health posters and coloured lines on the floor, all designed to instruct visitors and patients about how to negotiate the building and behave there. Unlike words spoken to individuals, their messages are addressed simultaneously to all hospital users, and they are perpetrated not even by the hospital itself but by a mysterious "NHS Trust". On a number of floors within the building, there are desks near the lifts where people may be found at certain hours of the day offering help and information to lost and baffled interlopers from the world outside. But significantly these desks are staffed not by the hospital itself, but by volunteers – the "Friends of the Royal Free". It is as if the *real* business of the hospital has nothing to do with talking to people and ensuring that their time spent there is as congenial and worry-free as possible. Helping people find their clinics, guiding them towards the lifts, informing them about parking arrangements, telling them about admission procedures are not part of the service. They can be left to others, not the paid staff, to provide.

Like all NHS institutions, the Royal Free does now have a "Patient

Advice and Liaison Service" (PALS) which offers information and assistance to patients and their relatives. However, this is located, not on a clearly visible desk near the hospital entrance, but in an enclosed office that is actually behind you as you enter the building and twist and turn your way towards the main lifts. Looking ahead as you endeavour to find your way through the maze of corridors, you will only ever see it on your way out. The positioning seems symbolic. It is somewhere you go not on arrival to ensure your visit runs smoothly, but as you leave to complain when things have gone wrong. The service is designed to assist with problems after they occur, not to try to prevent them happening in the first place.

Augé argues that "non-places" never exist in pure form, but that place and non-place are like opposed polarities: "If a place can be defined as relational, historical and concerned with identity, then a space which cannot be defined as relational or historical, or concerned with identity will be a non-place." So non-places, he suggests, partly as a result of their tendency to communicate through faceless texts, are ones that the individual experiences alone – where you find yourself solitary and isolated. Despite the abundance of people around you, you feel disconnected, unrelated to those with whom you share the environment. The single room of the business traveller in an international hotel; the supermarket aisle down which the shopper pushes his trolley; the vehicle in which the motorway driver is cocooned as she speeds on her way; the "cell" of the hospital bed from which the patient confronts his destiny: these are spaces of separation rather than meeting, places where you feel anonymous and apart, immersed in melancholy solitude.

For non-places are also ones where you are stripped of your individuality. "A person entering the space of non-places is relieved of his usual determinants. He becomes no more than what he does or experiences in the role of passenger, customer or driver." Or hospital patient, one might add. In non-places, identity is reduced to its official form: the passport that gives you access to the aeroplane, the credit card that permits you to pass through the supermarket checkout; the hospital number on the appointment letter that grants you a bed, and is also inscribed on the plastic name bands placed around your wrist and ankle on admission. In these environments you do not possess a full personality or complete identity, merely a numerical access code to be presented on entering or leaving. You are simply one of many drivers, hotel guests or hospital patients, without defining singularity.

In non-places, not only their users but the space itself is denuded of distinguishing character: "There is no room for history unless it has been transformed into an element of spectacle, usually in allusive texts. What reigns there is actuality, the urgency of the present moment." Like many hospitals, the Royal Free has a proud and noble history. It pioneered many of the precepts of inclusiveness and access for both patients and doctors that we now take for granted. However, little of this is apparent, other than on the sign-boards at the entrance to each ward which explain why it is named after Marsden, Jex-Blake or the Worshipful Company of Cordwainers. Perhaps it is the fact that the building is little more than 30 years old; perhaps it is because the NHS has made medical need rather than the ability to pay the criterion for admission to all hospitals these days; possibly it is due to the lack of women consultants, or the preference for announcing itself as a 15-year-old Trust rather than a 175-year-old Hospital: whatever the reason, it is hard to feel much connection between the bustling, faceless factory that is the Royal Free today with the illustrious history that constitutes its past. No vestiges of the blazing commitment to the financially and socially excluded, no legacy of its life-enriching zeal for emancipation and equality are to be found in the bland, all-purpose wish to be "an outstanding London teaching hospital recognized...for excellence in patient care, teaching and research" that now comprises its mission statement. It could be *any* hospital.

The non-place is "there to be passed through", not somewhere there is any reason – or you have any desire – to linger. Unlike the prison or the Foundling Hospital, which are places you *stay,* the modern hospital is a place through which you are processed, and which you *leave,* at the greatest possible speed. Between 1860 and 1980, expansion in healthcare provision meant increasing the number of hospital beds: the total in Britain per thousand of the population doubled between 1860 and 1940, and then doubled again between 1940 and 1980. Since 1980, however, while the number of senior hospital managers has increased 40-fold, the number of beds has significantly diminished, and the accent shifted to increasing capacity by ever more rapid patient turnover. Individual stays are abbreviated as patients are dealt with and discharged with industrial efficiency.

If non-places are ones that you pass through, then as a corollary to this, Augé suggests, they are also ones where you are never "at home". Although possessing a certain familiarity – derived partly from our constant exposure to them on television or through advertisements for airlines, hotels and supermarkets, and partly from their global homogeneity that dissolves national boundaries – non-places decline to offer us any sense of a world to which we belong. In an anthropological sense, home can be defined as a place where others speak our language:

"The sign of being at home is the ability to make oneself understood without too much difficulty and to follow the reasoning of others without any need for long explanations."

Quite apart from the babel of different languages and accents that assaults your ears as you enter most hospitals in Britain nowadays, as a patient or visitor you also have to contend with the acronyms, jargon and technical vocabulary that complicate communication and compromise understanding in any contemporary medical institution. "Is it an IM or IV injection?"; "Did the SHO recommend a CT or MRI scan?"; "Did you receive TPN feeding while you were in ITU?" This is beginner's level hospital-speak, which, after six months of living in Wonderland, I can just about follow. But put me in front of an episode of *ER* or *Casualty*, or assemble a surgical team around my bed, and I struggle to make sense of what is being said as much as the next person.

By just about every criterion that Augé proposes, the Royal Free – like every other large, modern hospital – is a non-place. A characteristic space of what he calls the supermodern age: a superhospital harbouring superbugs created by the supermodern world. There is nothing routine or commonplace here. Everything is excessive, "super" or larger than life. It is then perhaps a welcome development that the present trend in hospital building is away from monolithic superhospitals and towards complexes that are conceived on a less daunting and more human scale. The policy outlined in the 2006 White Paper on Health, which involves shifting many services away from big general hospitals and into community-based clinics, will also tend to erode the dominance of the superhospitals within the healthcare system and create smaller, more focused institutions. And this comes on top of a change that is already taking place in the way that

hospitals are funded: from April 2006 they ceased to receive block payments from Primary Healthcare Trusts, but began to be supported
instead by a system of payment per patient according to a set tariff for
the treatment provided. This will reinforce the historical drive for
greater efficiency by increasing patient turnover, and the thinking
behind it has already been apparent for some time at the Royal Free
where attempts to reduce the hospital's financial deficit were spear-
headed by a drive to cut the length of patient stays.

However, it is worth pausing to consider what kind of hospitals
these various changes are combining to create. The hospitals of the
future will be less community-based, since clinics will become the centres for local, routine care. Rather, the drift is towards increasingly
specialized hospitals, offering highly efficient and rapidly delivered
treatments – short stay "hotels" where we go for particular operations
and high-level care.

It is revealing that when the new University College Hospital
opened in London, the Trust Chairman proudly quoted in a newspaper article the comment of one local resident who had been to see the
new premises, which he described as "A state-of-the-art building, like
a five-star hotel". The "Hampstead Hilton" may be becoming less an
ironic sideswipe at the Royal Free's size and period architecture, and
more a straight description of the service it offers. For, ironically, the
trends in contemporary design and healthcare management are
making hospitals more like anonymous, corporate hotels – more like
non-places – than ever. The buildings may grow smaller, the facilities
be more upmarket – more single rooms, better televisions, glossier
paintwork – but to an increasing degree these will be places that you
pass through, rather than ones where you belong.

■ ■ ■

The question that needs to be asked is whether this is what we want
our hospitals to be? Certainly, it seems to correspond with the
patients' wishes. No one wants to stay in hospital longer than they
need to. But the problem is that this concept of the hospital is based on
a lie – or on what might be described as a "television drama" view of
what hospital stays actually involve. The factory idea of illness as
something that can be swiftly processed and resolved fails to

correspond with the reality of much medical care. Sadly, serious ill-nesses are not in general quickly cured; major operations are not always followed by painless and complication-free recoveries. The prison and refuge elements that underlie the hospital's history are, unfortunately but necessarily, still part of the package. So if hospitals abandon their traditions of caring in the ever more frantic pursuit of curing, then all we shall be left with when those cures fail to work instantly are cold and faceless prisons. There will be none of the comfort and compassion of the welcoming shelter when treatments prove prolonged.

What also needs to be remembered is that hospitals are where most of us die. When my mother's condition deteriorated to the point where she could no longer get out of bed and it would have been impossible for my father to continue looking after her at home, she promptly died the next day. But the majority of people are not so tidy or fortunate. They may wish to die at home, but fate and necessity will dictate otherwise. And even if more hospices are created to provide a more compassionate environment for those who are known to be terminally ill, death will still remain the ghostly counterpart, the "dark side", of all surgery and much other medical care. It is vital then for hospitals to be as much like home as possible, not places where you never are or can be "at home". They need to continue being charitable (i.e. loving) hostels where the sick and suffering can retreat for support, not become wards of heartless confinement where patients efficiently meet their institutional ends.

One of the more attractive analogies for the contemporary hospital that is coming into vogue is that of the health spa. Extending the hotel comparison, this suggests that the hospital should be a place to which you go for a variety of treatments that will strengthen and renew your body. It is an appealing idea, but a flawed and dishonest one. For hospitals, particularly in their evolving form, are not places for rest and pampering, but for bodily trauma. "Slash, trash and burn" is the vernacular slang for the most common forms of cancer treatment: surgery, chemotherapy and radiotherapy. This is the language of the battlefield, not the health spa. Hospital treatments, although generally bringing long-term benefits, leave the body battered and exhausted, not stimulated and refreshed like a luxurious massage or gentle aromatherapy session.

A couple I know well recently both had surgery in the space of the same week. The woman had an operation in a private hospital to repair cartilage in her knee that had been damaged in a skiing accident, and her partner underwent a vasectomy. They are intelligent, sensible people, but when I saw them the weekend following (both were already at home), I was struck by how surprised and rather shocked they seemed by the fact that they were in pain; and the woman – a mother with three small children – had clearly made no provision for being extremely tired, on crutches, and only able to move with difficulty. They had completely failed to anticipate the true meaning of their surgery.

As with the hotel analogy, likening the modern hospital to a spa is part of a dubious tendency to try to find commercial models for the services that hospitals provide. But while it is relatively straightforward to put a price on a bed for the night, or for a 30-minute facial, it is rather more problematic to do so in advance for a bowel re-section that might involve 11 nights care or five months. The problem is that we have such a confused idea of what hospitals are really like, and of the facilities and services that they can and do offer. On the one hand there is the TV drama image, which tidies up reality and raises expectations artificially high; on the other there is the image perpetrated by the press, which generally portrays them as dirty, infection-ridden, badly managed and uncaring.

The Royal Free offers a microcosm of this contradiction, and adds other confusions of its own. The hospital has been identified as one of the dirtiest in the country, with one of the highest rates of MRSA, but also one of the safest, with one of the lowest death rates. How do we make sense of that? Conclude that dirt is good for you? Question whether there is any direct link between cleanliness, MRSA and good health? Dismiss lists and league tables as meaningless and unhelpful? Or suggest that while the hospital's clinical care is good, possibly even outstanding given what it is up against, its ancillary and back-up services are terrible?

I believe that the last of these propositions is almost certainly the case, that the third has much to recommend it, and that the second may also contain a grain of truth: the relationship between hygiene and *Hygeia* (health), cleanliness and MRSA, is more complicated than is often suggested. However, the picture is clearly a messy one that resists easy interpretation, or reduction to glib metaphors. Many of the parallels used to describe the hospital scene seem to obscure the reality rather than reveal it. It is perhaps significant that 30 years ago hospitals frequently served as a metaphor for other things, notably society at large – hence the title of dramas such as Peter Nichols' *The National Health*. This identification of the hospital with the wider world forms part of a tradition that can be traced back at least to the 17th century, where it is found in John Donne's heartfelt cry: "As long as I remain in this great hospital, this sick, diseaseful world..."

More recently, however, the metaphors seem to have been reversed. Rather than describing other things as "like hospitals", we now describe hospitals as "like other things" – as though we have forgotten what a hospital itself is or should be. The identity of the institution appears to be in crisis, and it no longer seems sufficient to characterize a hospital without reference elsewhere, or to suggest that it should simply be first and foremost "like a hospital".

Faced with this confusion and loss of confidence, I find myself looking back on my experiences and asking what *I* want a hospital to be. What sort of Wonderland do I wish to find when I pass through the Royal Free's sliding entrance doors? Yes, an institution that is clear enough about its purpose to discard a lot of the metaphors that encumber it; a hospital that is comfortable being itself and caring for the sick, not aspiring to be something else, such as a spa or a trust. But, above all, I want it to be founded on the principle established by the proto-hospitals at the shrines of Asklepios in ancient Greece. I want it to be a place of healing.

CHAPTER
29

WHOLENESS

"Only connect! That was the whole of her sermon."
E M FORSTER Howards End

"And immediately the man was made whole, and took up his bed and walked"
St John, 5:9

The verb "to heal" shares a common root with the word "whole". In their original Germanic form, the two terms are essentially different grammatical parts of the same expression. Thus Jesus' injunction in the King James Bible, "Go in peace and be whole of thy plague", quite naturally becomes "Go in peace and be healed of your trouble" in the Good News version translated some 350 years later.

"Health" is another word with the same origins, and its underlying meaning might give us pause for thought if we substitute a synonym and start talking about the National Wholeness Service rather than the National Health Service. For if there is one attribute that the NHS seems to lack, it is wholeness in its other, complementary sense of completeness – the possession of all the requisite elements or parts as in "whole milk" or "whole nut chocolate".

For the patient, enjoying the benefits of the NHS is about negotiating a bewildering array of separate parts or institutions: GP surgeries, general and specialist hospitals, clinics for specific ailments, childcare or family planning centres, community services such as midwives or district nurses. Even a single hospital like the Royal Free is composed of an immense range of discrete departments and staff. I started my adventures there with a referral to a colorectal specialist in the Department of Surgery. But subsequent developments meant that I was handed on to the Gastroenterology Department for examination of my stomach problems; the Rheumatology Department for exploration of a possible tissue disorder; and another surgeon for treatment of my oesophageal stricture, which was actually undertaken by a consultant in the X-ray Department, and diagnosed by a specialist Speech and Language Unit at a different hospital entirely. In between times, as I have described, I saw and received assistance from a host of other people ranging from physiotherapists and dieticians to stoma nurses and palliative care doctors.

I have no complaint about the range and extent of the care that I have received, but as I progressed from department to department and saw one doctor or support worker after another, I increasingly felt that I was being viewed as a set of different parts or distinct ailments. No one seemed to be looking at the whole picture. Rather inconveniently, however – as my saga of side effects and complications bears all too eloquent witness – the body is not a collection of separate elements, but a unity. Although my own case might perhaps be regarded as unusual, the current tenacious hold of MRSA on our hospital services should serve as a sobering and unavoidable reminder that the different parts of the medical system do not exist in isolation, and that individual ailments cannot be treated without reference to and consideration of the whole pattern of care. It is tempting to view the "hospital superbug" as the human body's revenge for our daring to imagine that they could.

In Aleksandr Solzhenitsyn's novel *Cancer Ward*, there is a memorable scene where the talented and dedicated radiologist Ludmila Dontsova goes to visit her ageing mentor Oreshchenkov for a diagnosis of her own condition. Wearied by the sheer volume of her patients and their insistent demands, she complains about having to answer their constant, suspicious questions. To which the old man counters:

"'With the right kind of primary system, there'd be fewer cases altogether and no neglected ones. The primary doctor should have no more patients than his memory and personal knowledge can cover. Then he could treat each patient as a subject on his own. Treating diseases separately is work on the *feldscher* level…

'The patient's organism isn't aware that our knowledge is divided into separate branches. You see, the organism isn't divided. As Voltaire said, "Doctors prescribe medicine about which they know nothing for an organism about which they know less." How can we understand the patient as a single subject? After all, the anatomist who draws the charts operates on corpses; the living aren't his province, are they? A radiologist makes a name for himself on bone fractures; the gastro-intestinal tract is outside his field, isn't it? The patient gets passed from "specialist" to "specialist" like a basketball. That's why a doctor can remain a passionate bee-keeper, all through his career. If you wanted to understand the patient as a single subject, there'd be no room left in you for any other passion. That's the way it is. The doctor should be single subject as well. The doctor ought to be an all-rounder.'"

It is a provocative argument, which, perhaps significantly, comes from the mouth of a doctor who would have completed his training roughly 100 years ago. In the intervening period, medicine has grown increasingly specialized and continues to do so. I have no great affection for or attachment to the "superhospital" and its factory-monolith model of medical care. But the observation that "the organism isn't divided" seems to me profoundly true and important, and the sad and disturbing fact is that medical care is becoming ever more atomized and fragmented.

When faced with a major operation, long-term survival rates suggest that we should, quite rightly, seek out a consultant who specializes in that particular procedure, not opt for a general surgeon. It is equally reasonable that we should desire treatment, whenever possible, in small local clinics rather than in massive general hospitals designed to serve vast areas of the country. But both these demands intensify the drive towards healthcare that is more and more compartmentalized – a drive that gains even greater momentum as the NHS becomes increasingly marketized. For the trend in all markets is towards ever greater specialization as producers seek to maximize efficiency and profit margins. The same will be true of hospitals as they become funded on a payment per patient basis. An institution with particular expertise in, say, heart surgery will find itself able to offer that treatment more "efficiently" (i.e. cheaply and therefore profitably) than "rival" hospitals, and also on a more viable financial basis than it can perform other types of surgery. The result will be hospitals with fewer departments and increasingly narrow remits. This may produce gains in terms of strict cost effectiveness, but it has other implications of a much less desirable nature. For from the patient's point of view – as a single organism – there is a desperate need for connectedness. But if – as my experience demonstrates – that is hard to achieve within a single, present-day institution, it will be infinitely more so in a future system of healthcare staffed by narrowly focused doctors working in a plethora of discrete, highly specialized units. The bridling insistence of the Royal Free that I should have a further barium meal in its own X-ray Unit, rather than obtaining and accepting the results of the one I had at the Middlesex Hospital, is but one small example of how reluctant and unaccustomed different institutions are to work together. Disparate centres of care can make life extremely difficult for the patient, and may not ultimately serve his or her best interests.

When I worked as an in-house producer at the BBC in the late 1980s and early 1990s, one of the "tricks" of successful programme-making was to maximize your programme budget by off-loading costs wherever possible onto other departments. At its simplest, this meant sending scripts to actors coming in for audition by post rather than by motorcycle messenger. I was particularly insistent about this, since – whatever the occasional failings of the Royal Mail – the saving to the production was not just the difference between £10 or £15 for a bike and £2.50 for postage, but the difference between £10 or £15 and nothing at all. This was because the complication of charging individual items of mail to different cost centres meant that postage was paid for out of general overheads, not by individual programmes. Similarly, hotel and subsistence costs for staff working away from home were, for some peculiar reason, met by the design, camera or sound departments that employed them, not the production, which only paid for the actors, director and his or her assistants. Given that location fees were invariably much cheaper out of London, and that travel times could generally be reduced by filming out of the capital, this meant that it would often be cheaper for the production to shoot the programme in, say, Bristol or Bradford rather than within striking distance of Television Centre, even though the total cost to the BBC was actually greater.

There are comparable practices in the NHS today. Faced, like many hospitals recently, with an alarming budget deficit, the Royal Free developed plans to try to reduce the length of time that elderly patients in particular spend in hospital by encouraging social and community services to take responsibility for their care. As the hospital's Chief Executive is quoted as saying: "Our estimates show that an elderly person spends an average ten days in bed. We have 100 beds for the elderly. If we can reduce occupancy by ten per cent, to eight or nine days, then you may be able to free up ten beds." Money is saved for the hospital by shifting the cost of care to someone else. It is a classic case of "working the system" that is to be found in most large institutions. The difference between this and off-loading costs within the BBC, however, is that here people's lives and health are at stake. And having experienced the haphazard and inadequate support offered by the local health authority's district or community nurses, I have grave doubts about their ability to take on satisfactorily the extra demands that the hospital's new policy imposed upon them. Certainly if they are to do so, they will require more staff and resources, and it then becomes questionable whether the cost-cutting exercise by one institution will actually save money for the NHS as a whole. Once again, more fragmented care is likely to be detrimental to the patient, and it may not prove more efficient even in purely financial terms.

At the BBC, the introduction of cash accounting and a form of internal market through what was called "Producer Choice" (two related developments that were by no means in fact the same thing) served to eliminate some of the organization's more ridiculous anomalies and practices – only to replace them with a whole set of new ones. In the brave new world of competitive tendering, a production could save money by hiring a freelance designer for £1100 per week instead of paying £1200 for an in-house one; or obtain a cheaper camera package from a commercial supplier rather than use the Corporation's own equipment. But while this apparently reduced programme costs, it made no sense whatever for the BBC as a whole which found itself paying for the in-house designer to sit at home doing nothing as well as for the freelance one employed on the production. The "game" of shifting costs and squeezing the most out of your budget became ever more idiotic and cut-throat as the very existence of whole departments came under threat in consequence of the new arrangements.

When he became Director-General, Greg Dyke – who, whatever his editorial limitations, was by far the most talented manager to lead the BBC during the time I worked there – introduced a series of mantras to try and highlight areas in which the Corporation needed to amend and improve its performance. These included "Cut the Crap" (to be accompanied by waving a yellow card at managers in meetings who delayed or prevented action with bureaucratic waffle) and "One BBC". This catchphrase was designed to move staff beyond the fragmented thinking and destructive in-fighting that had increasingly become part of the Corporation's behaviour in the wake of its separation into different "business units", and to remind people that they all worked for the same organization whose interests needed to be considered as a whole. It is the kind of thinking that the NHS requires as it jettisons its planned economy and moves into an increasingly commercial system of management.

At present, reform of the NHS is producing a financial crisis characterized by a theoretically mind-bending excess of both demand *and* supply. On the one hand, thousands of patients continue to await treatment as referral times trim down, but waiting lists obstinately refuse to disappear as a problem; and on the other, hospitals, such as the Royal Free, are closing wards or instructing doctors to "go slow" because Primary Care Trusts cannot afford to pay for any more operations or treatment. This is a crazy and profligate waste of precious capital resources, but sadly all too typical of the clumsy way that artificial markets regulate themselves.

In the long run, the budgetary reforms being introduced into the NHS may reduce the cost per patient treated to the "customer" in the form of the Primary Healthcare Trusts. But whether this will represent real savings to the country and NHS as a whole is considerably more doubtful. While the "market" attempts to balance the capacity of the hospital system and the cash available to pay for it without even a free price mechanism to regulate its working, "inefficient" (or perhaps more accurately over-efficient) capacity will continue to remain unutilised. At the BBC, the illogic of maintaining a market system with a fixed resource base meant that the costume, design, make-up, camera and sound departments rapidly became unsustainable, and were duly closed down with thousands of staff being made redundant (many of whom were re-employed a few months later as freelances). But when the same thing happens in the Health Service, and hospitals start to go broke, who will pay off the creditors and make the necessary redundancy payments? It will inevitably be the NHS itself – or the taxpayer who funds it.

One of the mantras of office since New Labour came to power in 1997 has been "joined-up government". It is the national equivalent of "One BBC". But whether it is a question of securing more money for school dinners while millions are lavished on dealing with the consequences of obesity and poor diet; or the problem of ensuring that capital investment in the health service – either in hospital buildings and equipment or in expensively trained staff – is not idly squandered in pursuit of short-term cost-savings, "joined-up government" can prove extremely hard to achieve. Like the patient, healthcare services need to be thought about as a whole, not as a collection of disparate parts, but that grows increasingly difficult in a fragmented system of provision which is dominated by localized financial targets.

When I started producing at the BBC, and experienced at first hand its arcane and cumbersome machinery in action, I used to think that it was people, not systems, that mattered. Here was an appallingly designed system, yet somehow talented people managed to make it work and create wonderful programmes. But having seen what has happened to the quality of the Corporation's output over the past 15 years, as that system has been progressively dismantled, I am now less sure. At the very least, systems need to stay in place long enough for staff to learn how to get the best out of them. They also need to allow people the freedom to be able to do that. The highly interventionist, top-down management of a health service that is in a state of constant revolution and governed by questionable assumptions about efficiency and value for money may equally be making it difficult, if not impossible, for doctors to achieve the optimum quality of care within the resources available.

Of course, when you are ill you have little interest in the funding mechanisms and management systems that form the substance of health service politics. All you want (it sounds so simple) is ready access to doctors you trust, who can then use their knowledge, and possess the necessary resources, to make you better. Achieving this may be less straightforward, but clearly the key element is the relationships between yourself as a patient and the doctors who are treating you. These do not exist in a vacuum, however, and sadly they are unlikely to be improved by placing them on an increasingly commercial basis.

A year or two ago, I heard a lawyer friend, who is the senior partner of a successful firm of solicitors in the City of London, discussing the course of his career. "Thirty years ago I joined a profession," he said in voice tinged with loss and regret. "Today I run a business." His is an experience that many have shared over the same period, whether lawyers, (head) teachers, accountants – or doctors. And it is not solely to do with rising seniority. GP surgeries are now small businesses, with the doctors' salaries dependent on the profit earnt for services provided once the costs of running the practice have been deducted. Hospital consultants are now responsible for the income of the institutions in which they work, since that is directly determined by the number of patients they treat. In medicine, as in other realms, the idea of a vocation, of a commitment to an ideal such as justice, financial probity or the art of healing, is increasingly submerged under financial imperatives as the work into which it translates is increasingly reframed as a financial transaction. There may have been something dishonest in the gentlemanly pretence that professional activity and advice had nothing to do with anything so vulgar as money. But it is no more a true reflection of the relationship between doctor and patient to regard it purely as a service to be bought and consumed. Regret is commonly expressed about the rise of a "compensation culture", but this is simply the flip-side of reducing so many of our human relationships to commodities to be bought and sold. If the goods prove faulty or disappoint, the purchaser will naturally seek recompense. Ironically, it is often those expressing loudest regret for the boom in negligence claims who are also most vociferous in demanding that the health service should be "opened up to the market". What they fail to recognize is the risk and imprecision that so much medicine entails. There is a lack of certainty about medical outcomes, which we all instinctively recognize, but which regarding treatment as a simple financial transaction – along with a host of other factors at work in our present-day culture – inevitably tends to obscure.

When I was a teenager, I heard a distinguished consultant surgeon from Hammersmith Hospital give a memorable explanation of why the evangelical charity The Mission to Lepers had changed its name to the Leprosy Mission in an attempt to combat the stigmatisation of those afflicted with the disease. "There's a lesson for us all in that," he declared passionately. "It's so easy to talk about 'this bronchitic'. That's just as thoughtless and harmful as calling someone 'this leper'. He isn't a bronchitic. He's a man with bronchitis. The other is a man with leprosy. We must always remember that." His diatribe calls to mind the famous dictum of Sir William Gull: "Never forget that it is not pneumonia, but a pneumonic man who is your patient." These days doctors may not often talk of bronchitics and lepers, but we all routinely refer to heart patients, kidney patients, cancer patients. They're not. They are men with heart disease, women with kidney problems, children with cancer. Their identities are not synonymous with the diseases from which they are suffering, and they will all respond to treatment in their own uniquely individual ways. As Raymond Tallis has put it in his book *Hippocratic Oaths*:

> "The recent emphasis on narrative-based medicine, taking
> account of individual characteristics of patients, is a healthy
> corrective to the notion that medical practice can be reduced to
> a series of algorithms. While evidence-based medicine is a
> *necessary* condition of good medical care, it is not a *sufficient*
> condition."

Good medicine is about treating individuals as complex wholes ("individual subjects"), not dealing with diseases as abstract phenomena with failsafe remedies offering guaranteed outcomes. But by the same token, if the patient needs to be regarded as a complete person, then so does the doctor. The physician's expertise and caring should not be reduced to a hollow equation of time, information and skill that can be measured in purely monetary terms. The relation between doctor and patient is at best one of the noblest and most complex interactions of which humanity is capable. As one patient put it, whom I overheard at Mr Thomas's clinic: "I really trust that man. He's had his hands inside me." Few other relationships – other than sexual ones – embrace that degree of intimacy, commitment and care. It is about prolonging and enriching human life, not paying a few pounds to replace a broken car part which we lack the time or training to do ourselves (and as anyone who has had a car will know, even finding the cause of a malfunctioning engine and fixing it may not be without its complications).

■ ■ ■

The heroic age of medicine is over. In the same way that we now regard politicians, lawyers, journalists and almost any other group one cares to name with suspicion and cynicism, we no longer believe in or trust doctors in the way that we did 40 years ago in the days of *Dr Kildare*. The reasons for this are many and woven deep into the fabric of recent history, but the development is perhaps not wholly to be lamented. If doctors have proved to be human and flawed, and are no longer heroes, then patients may no longer be forced into the role of shadows. The way may be open to reformulate the relationship between doctor and patient as one between two fallible but fully contributing individuals who are seeking a commonly desired outcome. It may be free for us to re-conceive our hospitals as institutions appropriate for an age of mistrust and anxiety.

If we look for models of how to do this, yet again the treatment of people suffering from cancer seems to suggest a positive way forward. Whether it is because the area is better funded and resourced, the fact that the gravity of the illness and looming presence of death that accompanies it encourage greater consideration and respect, or for some other reason, there does appear to be a more integrated system of care for cancer than is to be found elsewhere in the pattern of healthcare provision. Marcus Conant, who was among the pioneers of

AIDS treatment at San Francisco General Hospital, perceptively iden-tified the problem: "one of the things that medicine does well is communicate vertically; one of the things it does badly is communicate horizontally." Cancer treatment, along with the care for AIDS patients, has gone a long way towards addressing this problem and ensuring much greater co-ordination of resources. In so doing, AIDS care in particular has also helped to re-define the roles of physician and patient.

When I was first discharged from the Royal Free, although my cancer was nominally cured as a result of surgery, my GP put me in touch with the Palliative Care Team at the Middlesex Hospital on account of their expertise in juggling drugs to deal with nausea. In fact they had limited success with me on this front, but from my point of view it was still an inspired referral. Nurses, doctors, even a consultant came to visit me at home to discuss my problems and needs – and, unlike the district nurses they actually turned up when they said they would. When the discharges from my fistula became unbearable, they promptly organized a delivery of drugs, syringes and needles to help alleviate the difficulty. When I went to Cornwall and developed a slightly alarming stomach infection, a phone call to their office brought not only reassurance but precise instructions about what to do. Through the mediation of Maggie, the genial and quietly authori-tative consultant nurse, I was made aware of an immense range of resources and services that were available to me, and given grief-free access to them. As I grew stronger, she organized a physiotherapist to come and visit me at home, who in turn arranged for me to use the gym at a local hospice. She offered counselling to Anna and myself with a trained member of the Palliative Care Team. She liaised with my GP about the possibilities of obtaining vitamin and mineral supple-ments on prescription. In short, she acted as intermediary and guide to a multi-faceted network of practical care and support, identifying serv-ices and possibilities of which I had no knowledge, and smoothly arranging for me to enjoy their benefit.

There is a suggestion that when patients are referred for hospital treatment, they should first be seen by a general physician who then co-ordinates the different forms of specialist care that the institution has to offer. In a world of increasingly complicated and fragmented medical services, the idea has much to recommend it. Faced with frightening illness and a baffling hospital system of which we have little knowledge or understanding, we would all appreciate and benefit from a friendly guide to show us the route back to health – a doctor who regards us as a whole person, and looks at the entire picture, not just the separate parts. This figure might be a better equipped and less hard-pressed GP, but I suspect it needs to be someone who is actually inside the hospital system.

The future may not be so much about the doctor-patient relationship as about the doctors-patient relationship – an extension of what has long been the case, whereby it is teams of different carers who are responsible for our welfare, not just single individuals. Under these circumstances, what we require is not so much a hero – there are a host of talented people who will play their particular part in combating our illness – but rather a wise and empathetic spirit, someone we trust who can introduce us to the many august but unfamiliar figures we may meet on our journey. A Virgil to our benighted Dante, who is able to lead us through Hell and Purgatory, and back once more to Paradise.

CHAPTER
30

ENVOI: HOME

"All is flux, nothing stays still."
HERACLEITUS Fragments of the Pre-Socratics

This is a story without a proper ending. Happily, in some ways, there is no real narrative closure, no final conclusion or point of rest; only a messy tangle of loose ends, a shifting sea of unfinished business. Although I may have often doubted it during my faltering, stalled convalescence, the world turns and everything changes. In drawing this chronicle to a close, all I can do is record the situation in which I find myself today, aware that tomorrow this reality may be transformed and the story assume a very different complexion.

The Royal Free is part of the process. A number of the things I have described in these pages have already changed in the period since I began writing. Mr Thomas has lost weight, for instance. He remains a giant of a man, but his outsize hands now have the slender elegance of a woman's. Flowers have been banned from the wards, with the result that the shop in the entrance hall is no longer "June's Flowers" but a gift emporium run by the Friends of the Royal Free. As the hospital continues its constant programme of refurbishment, better waiting areas have been created in the CT scan and Endoscopy departments, although elsewhere the arrangements remain as provisional and uncomfortable as ever. One of the more encouraging and impressive aspects of the Royal Free is its unremitting attempts at self-improvement. Following many complaints and some negative publicity in the press about the difficulty of getting through the switchboard to make appointments (which are deemed unwanted if not accepted within a fixed time-period), the hospital has purchased extra phone lines and recruited additional staff to help the referral system run more smoothly. It has also put aside an extra £500,000 in 2006/7 to improve what it describes as "hotel services such as portering". Depressingly, it seems unaware that the only similarity between hospital and hotel porters is an accident of nomenclature. And when I recently needed a further oesophageal dilatation, the request for an appointment somehow got lost in the system, resulting in a distressing delay that I only managed to unlock by recruiting the assistance, yet again, of my old ally Gabriella, the colorectal nurse. "Plus ça change, plus c'est le même chose," might be the cynic's response, but the truth is actually more complicated and subtle than that.

What indisputably has changed is that I am writing this, not incarcerated in hospital, but at home, sitting in my own garden. It is high summer. The flowers that surround me are in full bloom. The sun is shining. The leaves on the trees are swaying and rustling in the breeze. The air is balmy, fragrant with the scent of jasmine. Alas, the peace and tranquillity of the morning are being disturbed by the sounds of banging and a piercing electrical saw from building work in the house next door. If this is paradise – and in some sense it most certainly is – there are sadly still serpents lurking in the undergrowth.

Anna is at work, but the strains of having had cancer, nursing me through my illness, raising our children, and earning a living to keep us all, have taken their toll. Although becoming less frequent, she is still prey to occasional bouts of post-viral exhaustion that have plagued her for the past two years. She also has a bothersome ovarian cyst, which may soon require surgery or other treatment. A short while ago, however, she did receive a "five-year clear" for her cancer, which puts her among the modest percentage with her particular form of the disease who survive that long after surgery. It was the cause for some gratitude and quiet pleasure, but we did not feel inclined to crack open the champagne. Although after five years the doctors consider that particular episode to be over, they never regard cancer as "cured". The shadow may recede, but it does not disappear entirely. Nevertheless, the extent of her recovery to date – the fullness and intensity of the life she is currently leading – remains little short of miraculous.

Our sons appear to have weathered the ordeal of watching both their parents fall ill in grim succession with their well-being relatively intact. They may have been protected in part by the immersion in the immediacy of the moment that is one of the features and joys of childhood, and are perhaps even the stronger for their experience. Edmund, the younger boy, does grow slightly, but perceptibly, anxious each time I return to hospital for yet another procedure. But whether they both bear deeper scars that are yet to reveal themselves, time alone will tell.

I remain haunted by my time in hospital, and by the many strange dreams or hallucinations that I had there. I generally have little recall of my dreams, but these feverish imaginings are unfadingly vivid, if strangely difficult to put into words. In one I am riding a tricycle into the sky, rising higher the faster I pedal. When I reach a certain level, I begin to hear the music of the heavens, echoing from the mountain tops over which I am passing. As I ascend, the volume swells, and the music grows progressively more intense, harmonious and magnificent. In another fantasy, I am trapped between two valleys in a dark, gothic landscape. In a third, I am travelling on a speeding, ultra-modern train, slumbering in a comfortable bed as the carriages sweep across a huge, flat plain in America, tracing an undeviating line of unbelievable length and straightness. Others involve attacking an imaginary walled city of Calais by walking across the English Channel as part of some medieval army that displays the buccaneering bravado of the invading forces in Shakespeare's *Henry V;* and drifting back to England on the incoming tide after a holiday abroad, before making my way into a deserted night-time customs' shed. I can find few sources for these dreams in my waking life, and I struggle to interpret or understand them. Although I occasionally search for some significance in their curious images and disjointed narratives, any meaning I find always seems external and imposed. For that reason, they are perhaps the true imaginative residue of my time in hospital; I used to joke that during my near-death experiences I never saw a white-bearded figure at the end of a long tunnel beckoning me towards him, but in truth these imaginings are every bit as strange.

Looking at photographs of myself now, I find it hard to recognize the gaunt, stooping figure who confronts me. Mentally I feel much as I ever did, so am perplexed by the shrunken appearance of my body. I have regained half the weight I lost, and currently tip the scales at a little over nine stones. It is a very crude barometer, but I feel it roughly reflects the extent of my recovery. I am far more active than I was: I do most of the family cooking, get out a fair amount, have started travelling abroad again, and managed to write this book. But returning to full-time employment remains a distant prospect: I still sleep after lunch most days (well, so did Churchill, one might say); I also need to sit quietly after eating, and continue to experience erratic, unpredictable bouts of nausea. My stamina and strength are severely limited; my body is not reliable. The consolation is that, against the odds and albeit by the tiniest of increments, my condition continues to improve. Four years after leaving hospital, my body is still healing itself. In an oscillating progression, my weight creeps gradually upwards. Although I seem to hit periodic plateaux, I do not sense that I have yet reached the limit of my recovery.

My stomach, however, still looks like the gory remains of a car crash, with two lumps of intestine hanging out of the abdomen wall. I face two further operations if they are to be repaired and put back in place. And my surgical wound continues to discharge a bloody mucous. There is an internal leakage causing this that also requires surgery. In addition, every few months my gullet shrivels to the point where eating becomes problematic and requires stretching to open it up again. Like Odysseus, who on his eventual return to Ithaca still faces further journeys to propitiate the gods, my travels are not over. I may be home, but must go away again, at least for a time.

I occasionally wonder whether Anna and I are extremely unlucky to have both been struck down by serious illness at so young an age; or whether we are extremely lucky since, at least for the moment, we have both survived our ordeal. Although the propositions are apparently opposed, both are of course true. Like most people who have experienced similar fates, I carry the contradiction within me as the reality of my existence. Instinctively, as part of the daily fabric of my life, I am more inclined to consider myself fortunate; it is only when I stop to think about what has happened that I have feelings of self-pity or a resentful sense of life's unfairness. Unsurprisingly, therefore, I try not to think about it.

Edmund leaves primary school this year, and last night I went to see him play Bagheera in his class's farewell production of *The Jungle Book*. Watching your child on stage seems to unlock any parent's emotions, and my feelings as he stood centre stage, beaming while he led the curtain call, were ones of untrammelled pleasure and delight. When I was in hospital, having just survived my own brush with death, the father of one of his classmates – with whom I had manned the entrance at several of the school's Christmas fairs – received some medication for depression that completely unhinged him. Without presentiment or warning, he walked off a cliff and died. Phil was not there yesterday to enjoy seeing his daughter perform. Illness brings home the precariousness and fragility that underpins all our lives. The ground may disappear beneath our feet at any time. But today, for all the anguish and heartache, there are still moments of ineffable sweetness to be relished and savoured. The challenge for us all is to make the most of them.